最新美國口語俚語精選

Modern American
Slang and Colloquialisms

黃希敏　編著

國立中央圖書館出版品預行編目資料

最新美國口語俚語精選：Modern American
slang and colloquialisms／黃希敏編著.
修訂版. --臺北市：書林，民82
143 面：21 公分
ISBN 957-586-389-5（平裝）

1.英國語言--俗語,俚語

805.138　　　　　　　　　　　82007391

最新美國口語俚語精選

定價：125 元　　　卡帶兩捲：300 元

作　　者／黃希敏

插　　畫／李建興

執行編輯／王添源

出 版 者／書林出版有限公司

　　　　　台北市新生南路三段88號二樓之五

　　　　　電話：3687226　Fax：3636630

發 行 人／蘇正隆

郵　　撥／15743873・書林出版有限公司

印　　刷／國榮印刷廠

登 記 證／局版臺業字第一八三一號

中 華 民 國 八 十 年 三 月 一 版
中 華 民 國 八 十 二 年 十 二 月 修 訂 一 刷

ISBN 957-586-389-5
© 1991.3, 1991.8, 1993.12（修訂一刷）

編　者　序

　　美國對我而言，不僅是留學經驗，更是生活經驗。從加州到德州，十五年間，這個地方提供我制度化、高效率的社會、日新月異的資訊、百家爭鳴的氣氛，這樣的環境，對於我"先天"的最愛——語言，自是一片沃土。我看電視、跟美國朋友談話，往往一本筆記在手，隨時記下以往不曾用過的語句。美國的電視從早到晚有看不完的好節目，知識性的、教育性的、娛樂性的……，就像是我的免費家教，天天把政治人物、專家學者、以至於尋常百姓，帶到我眼前，就各種大小問題發表言論。從他們的談話中，我看見美語的最近趨勢、最道地用法，這種學習，是我長久以來的嗜好，於是口語筆記一本本，猶如果實一籮筐一籮筐，真想與在其他地方勤學美語的朋友分享。

　　返台任教這段期間，發現國內類似的書不少，卻都失之老舊，於是把自己手邊的稿子先整理出一部分，彙編成冊，並請輔大英語系畢業的李建興先生作插畫，增加趣味，以利記憶。相信此書對於有志熟悉今日美語的學生以及社會人士，都會有莫大助益。

黃希敏

1.15.1991 於休士頓

最新美國 口語俚語 精選

修訂版

黃希敏　編著

李建興　插畫

across the board　全盤的；全面的

Everyone in the corporation received an across the board increase in salary. 公司裡每個人都加薪。

act up

√ **act up　胡鬧；出毛病**

The children started to act up as soon as the teacher left the room. 老師一離開教室，孩子們就鬧起來了。

√ I was late to work this morning because the car acted up and wouldn't start. 我今天早上因車子出毛病而上班遲到。

ad lib　即興而作，隨口編

The comedian ad libbed most of his routine. 那個笑匠的台詞多半是隨口編的。

√ **add insult to injury　越搞越糟；越描越黑**

Her awkward attempt to explain her error merely added insult to injury. 她笨拙地解釋錯誤，結果越描越黑。

ahead of the game　領先；佔優勢

Marsha got ahead of the game by finishing her work early. Marsha 因提早完成工作而領先他人。

airbrain／airhead　呆子

Joyce can't understand anything. She's such an airbrain.
Joyce 什麼都不懂，她是個呆子。

all ears　全神貫注

Whenever you tell Johnny some gossip, He's all ears.　每當
你說閒話給 Johnny 聽時，他總是全神貫注。

all ears

all hell broke loose　一團糟

When the flood hit, all hell broke loose.　洪水一氾濫，一切亂
糟糟。

all-out　盡力，全力以赴

The team made an all-out effort to win the game.　這支隊伍
全力以赴以贏得比賽。

all right already　好啦好啦，別唸啦

All right already, I'm coming !　好啦好啦，別唸啦，我來了！

all the way　毫無保留

I'll back her all the way.　我會自始至終支持她的。

all thumbs　笨手笨腳的；笨拙的

I'm all thumbs when it comes to sewing.　說起做女紅，我是非
常笨拙的。

all wet 　錯誤的

I'm afraid your idea is all wet. 　我想你的想法是不對的。

all wet

along for the ride 　隨著他人走，看看 [不怎麼認真地參與一事]

Don't mind me. I'm just along for the the ride. 　別管我，我只是看看而已。

antsy 　[出自 have ants in one's pants] 焦躁不安

After waiting around for so long, Paul started to get antsy. 等了這麼久，Paul 開始焦躁不安。

antsy

A-OK 　[ˈeˌoˈke] 情況順利；進行良好

He was A-OK after the surgery. 　他手術後情況很好。

an arm and a leg 　昂貴的價格

This furniture cost me an arm and a leg, but it was worth it. 這件家具花了我一大筆錢，但是很值得。

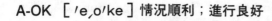

as...as all get out ......極了

Mother is as mad as all get out.　母親氣瘋了。

as is　（物品）照原狀［不做修理或改進］

The salesman said I could buy the car for $500 as is, or give him $1,200 after he fixes all its problems.　售貨員說我可以以 500 元按現在的樣子買這部車，或是給他 1,200 元把所有的毛病修理好。

asap　立刻；馬上［出自 as soon as possible］

Hurry up! I need that report asap.　快點！我馬上要那份報告。

ask for it　自找麻煩；罪有應得

You were asking for it by driving around with bad brakes. 開煞車失靈的車是你自找麻煩。

ask for it

awesome　棒極了

That was an awesome party. Everybody had fun.　邪個宴會棒極了，每個人都玩得很高興。

back off　緩和；軟化；減輕

The city council had to back off from its criticism of the utility department.　市議會必須減輕對公共事業部門的批評。

B

back out 退出(交易)；叫停

George backed out of the deal at the last minute. George 在最後一刻退出交易。

back, put something on the back burner 暫時擱置

Paul was so busy that he had to put several projects on the back burner. Paul 忙得必須把幾個計劃暫時擱置下來。

backseat driver 喜歡在後座指導人家如何開車的人；不在其位而謀其政

Please be quite. I can't concentrate with so many backseat drivers in the car. 安靜點，那麼多人指揮，我無法專心開車。

backseat driver

back at ／ to square one 回到起點，白費力氣

It's really frustrating! After so much effort, I'm back at square one. 真洩氣！我費了那麼多力氣結果是白忙一場。

bad 太棒了 [講反話]

That outfit is bad. Where can I get one? 那套衣服棒透了，那裡可以買到？

bad blood 嫌隙；不和；敵意

Ever since Howard borrowed 5,000 dollars from Mike and

never paid him back, there has been bad blood between them.
自從 Howard 向 Mike 借了 5,000 元不還之後，他們之間就有了嫌隙。

bad-mouth　說壞話

Paul was always bad-mouthing his superiors until his boss threatened to fire him.　老闆威脅要炒 Paul 魷魚，他才停止說老闆壞話。

bad news　討厭鬼

Marcy is nothing but bad news around here.　Marcy 眞是這一帶的的討厭鬼。

ballpark figure　大約數目；略估

I think it will cost you about 50 dollars, but that's a ballpark figure.　我想它大約要花你 50 元。

ballpark figure

baloney　胡扯

Baloney! I never said that.　胡扯！我從沒那麼說。

bananas　瘋子

The guy acts like he's bananas.　這傢伙舉動像個瘋子。

bank on　信任；倚賴

The public knew they could bank on the mayor to do what he promised.　群眾知道他們能信任市長會實現承諾。

bank on

bar none　只此一家，別無分號

This is the best ice cream anywhere in the state of Texas, bar none.　這是德州最好的冰淇淋，別無分號。

barf　嘔吐

When Amy was sick, she barfed all night.　Amy 生病，吐了一晚。

barge in　闖入

Geroge rudely barged in on our private meeting.　George 無禮地闖入我們的私下會談。

basket case　絕望無助、意志消沈的人

When Sam's wife left him, he was a basket case for weeks.　Sam 的太太離開他時，他消沈了好幾個星期。

beat a dead horse　白費唇舌，白費力氣

I've already made up my mind. There's no sense beating a dead horse.　我已經下了決心，不必再白費唇舌了。

beat it 走開

Beat it! I'm busy right now. 走開！我現在忙著。

beats me 我不知道

Beats me. We haven't learned that yet. 我不知道，我們還沒有學到那個。

beats me

beeswax 〔bízwæks〕 事情 ［出自 business ］

This is a private matter. It's none of your beeswax. 這是個人的事，和你無關。

belly laugh 震耳欲聾的笑聲

My goodness, Burt, you've got a real belly laugh. 天哪，Burt，你的笑聲真震耳。

belly up 垮了；死了；完蛋 ［源於〝死魚肚子向上〞］

The restaurant went belly up after being open for only three months. 這家餐廳才開張三個月就倒了。

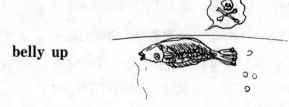

belly up

bent out of shape　氣壞了；大發雷霆

Mother is really bent out of shape because we came home so late last night.　我們昨晚遲歸，母親大發雷霆。

bend over backwards　不遺餘力

Sue will bend over backwards to help her friends.　Sue 會盡全力幫助朋友。

between a rock and a hard place　進退兩難

I don't know what the solution is. Right now, I'm caught between a rock and a hard place.　我不知道如何解決，現在我進退兩難。

between a rock and
a hard place

big　重要的；受歡迎的，熱門的

Michael Jackson is a big name in the music business. Michael Jackson 在音樂界是個響噹噹的名字。

Her new novel is really big in New York.　她的新小說在紐約很紅。

big deal　重要的事

It's no big deal. I don't mind helping you out.　這沒什麼大不了的，我不介意幫助你。

big idea, What's the big idea?　什麼意思?!

What is the big idea? I don't appreciate all the personal questions.　什麼意思?!　我可不喜歡被問這些私人問題。

big league, hit the big leagues ／ time　更上一層樓

He's not a small time accountant anymore. With his new job, he's definitely hit the big leagues.　他不再是個小會計了，有了新工作，他的確更上一層樓。

big man on campus　學生領袖；校園風雲人物

Rick is the captain of the football team. He's the big man on campus.　Rick 是足球隊長，是校園風雲人物。

big picture　（事情的）主要部份；重點

Concentrate on the big picture for now. Don't worry about the minor details.　先把精神集中在重點上，不要擔心次要的細節。

big cheese

big shot（＝ VIP, big cheese, big wheel）　大人物，大頭

You can tell John is a big shot; he rides in a limousine

everywhere he goes. 你可以看出 John 是個大人物，無論去那裡他都坐豪華轎車。

big stink／fuss 大大數落；大驚小怪

The teacher made a big stink over my being late to class. 我上課遲到被老師嘮叨了一頓。

bimbo 放蕩的女人

The man thought Elaine was a bimbo because of the way she flirted with him. 這個人因為 Elaine 挑逗他的樣子而認為她是不正經的女人。

binge 持續吃喝狂鬧

Betty has been on a binge for four days now. Betty 已經連續四天大吃大喝。

binge

birdbrain 白癡

Joy is a real birdbrain in some ways. Joy 在某方面是不折不扣的白癡。

bitch 臭美的女人

Joann thinks she owns the world. She's a real bitch. Joann 認為整個世界都是她的，真是臭美。

bite the bullet　咬緊牙關；忍受痛苦

You just bite the bullet and get it over with.　咬緊牙關完成這件事吧！

bite the dust　死亡；報銷

This pen just bit the dust.　這枝鋼筆報銷了。

In Western movies, the bad guys bite the dust regularly.　西部電影裡，壞人通常會完蛋。

bite the dust

blabbermouth　大嘴巴；愛說閑話的人

I don't like Don because he's a blabbermouth.　我不喜歡 Don，因爲他愛說人閑話。

black and white　①白紙黑字　②涇渭分明

Mrs. Jones did not believe the news, so Mr. Jones showed her the article in the newspaper and said, "There it is in black and white." Jones 太太不相信這消息，所以 Jones 先生給她看報上的文章說：「在這裡白紙黑字寫著。」

Bill sees everything as black and white. If you're not his friend, you're his enemy.　Bill 事事涇渭分明，如果你不是他的朋友，就是他的敵人。

black out　昏倒；喪失記憶

It was so hot and stuffy in the room that she blacked out.
房裡悶熱得讓她昏倒了。

black out

blah-blah-blah　說個不停

All she does is go "blah-blah-blah" all night, but she never says anything worth remembering the next morning.　她整夜說個不停，但沒有一句值得記到第二天早上的話。

blast　極好的東西

That party was a blast.　這次舞會眞是棒極了。

blast

bleeding heart　濫好人

The liberal candidate was accused by his conservative opponent of being a bleeding heart on welfare issues.　自由派候選人被保守派對手在福利問題上斥爲濫好人。

blockbuster　極叫座的電影表演

The Godfather was a blockbuster in the U.S.　教父在美國相當叫座。

blockhead　笨蛋

Arnold is a blockhead if I ever saw one.　Arnold 是我見過最笨的人。

blow it　搞砸了；弄壞了

I blew it on that last exam.　我上次考試考砸了。

blow it

blow off steam　（亦作 let off steam）　發洩悶氣

Don't pay any attention to him. He's just blowing off steam. 不要管他，他不過是發洩一下悶氣罷了。

blow one's cool　亂了方寸

Patty blew her cool when everyone started laughing at her. 大家開始笑 Patty 時，她就亂了方寸。

blow one's cover　洩底

The detective was careful not to let the drug dealer know he worked for the police. He didn't want to blow his cover. The drug dealer thought the detective was a junkie.　偵探小心不讓毒販知道他替警方工作，他不想洩漏身分。毒販以爲偵探是個毒癮客。

blow one's top ／ stack ／ wig ／ cork　氣瘋了

The boss blew his top when he found out about the robbery.
老闆發現搶劫時氣瘋了。

blow the lid off　揭發（醜聞）

That newspaper story blew the lid off the Senator's illegal
business deals.　報紙的報導揭發了參議員的非法勾當。

blow the lid off

blow the whistle on　揭露；告發

Michael blew the whistle on the corporation's plan to by-
pass anti-pollution laws.　Michael揭露公司罔顧反污染法律的計劃。

blowup　失和；口角

Frank and I had a blowup last night.　Frank 和我昨夜吵了一
架。

BLT　燻肉加上萵苣和番茄做成的三明治〔bacon, lettuce, and
tomato〕

I'm in the mood for a sandwich. I think I'll have a BLT. 我想
吃三明治，我要一個BLT。

blue in the face　臉都綠了；筋疲力盡

Matt blew up balloons for the party until he was blue in the face.　Matt 一直爲晚會吹氣球，吹到臉都綠了。

blue in the face

boat, rock the boat　壞事，自找麻煩

The other boys said that Henry was rocking the boat by wanting to let girls join their club.　其他男孩說亨利要讓女生加入俱樂部是自找麻煩。

rock the boat

bogue　假惺惺

Craig can be really bogue at times. I wish he'd stop telling those disgusting stories.　Craig 有時眞是假惺惺，我希望他不要再說那些噁心的故事了。

bogus　假的

This is a bogus five-dollar bill.　這是五元的僞鈔。

bonehead　笨蛋

Paula is a bonehead; she can't do anything right.　Paula 是個笨蛋，什麼事都做不對。

boo-boo　①錯誤②［孩童語］傷疤

① Sorry, I made a boo-boo.　抱歉，我弄錯了。

② David got a boo-boo on his knee from falling off the swing.　David 從鞦韆跌下來，膝蓋上留下一個難看的疤。

boob, the boob tube (the tube)／the idiot box　電視

She's watching the boob tube right now.　她正在看電視。

boogie〔búgi〕(= booger〔búgə〕)　鼻屎

It's impolite to pick your nose and play with your boogies. 挖鼻孔和玩鼻屎是不禮貌的。

book, by the book　照規矩做

We're not going to skip any steps on this project. We're going to do everything strictly by the book.　這件事我們不會省略任何步驟，一切都照規距做。

by the book

born loser 天生輸家；注定要失敗的人或事；扶不起的阿斗

I feel sorry for Roger. No matter how hard he tries, he's just a born loser. 我爲 Roger 難過，不管他怎麼努力，就是不行。

bottom line 總之；歸根結底

The bottom line is that our sales need to pick up if we're going to make a pofit this year. 總之，如果我們今年要獲利的話，銷售量一定得增加。

bow out 不幹了；退出

Mr. Black often quarreled with his partners, so he finally bowed out of the company. Black 先生經常和合夥人爭吵，因此他終於退出了公司。

While the movie was being filmed, the star got sick and had to bow out. 電影拍攝當中，明星演員生病了，必須退出。

bow out

bozo 笨蛋；傻瓜

What a bozo! He can't tell his left from his right. 真是個笨蛋！他左右不分。

brainstorm ①好主意②腦力激盪

① I just had a brainstorm! We can all go in my car! 我有個好主意！大家都搭我的車去。

② Let's brainstorm and see if we can come up with some

new ideas. 讓我們腦力激盪一下看看能不能有新點子。

break, give someone a break 鬆口氣

The boss gave her a break and let her try again. 老闆讓她鬆口氣，讓她再試一次。

give someone a break

break a leg 祝演出成功〔表面意思 "摔斷腿" 的反話〕

I know you're going to be great in the play tonight. Break a leg! 我知道你今天晚上的演出會很成功，祝你順利！

break a leg

break in 使適應；使進入狀況；磨合（汽車引擎）

New shoes are stiff until you break them in. 新鞋合脚前都是硬梆梆的。

It takes time to break in a new employee. 引導新職員進入情況得花點時間。

break it up　停止談天、吵架、打架 [原意爲"分開"]

Break it up! I will not permit fighting in this classroom.　住手！我不准有人在教室裡打架。

break out　逃出

The inmates planned to break out of jail after midnight.　犯人計劃午夜後逃出監獄。

breaks, the breaks　運氣不佳

Sorry, Susie, that's the breaks.　Susie，抱歉，運氣實在不好。

the breaks

break someone up　笑死人

John can really break me up sometimes.　John 有時眞把我笑死。

break the news to　告訴壞消息

Paul had to break the news of her friend's death to Paula.　Paul 必須告訴 Paula 她朋友的死訊。

breed, a new breed of　新生代

America is experiencing a new breed of ambitious and edu-
cated, young businessmen.　美國出現了一批雄心勃勃、教育水準高
的新生代企業家。

breeze (= piece of cake)　輕而易舉的事

This job is a breeze.　這件工作輕而易舉。

breeze

bright-eyed and bushy-tailed　精神奕奕

Joanna always shows up at work bright-eyed and bushy-
tailed.　Joanna 工作時總是精神奕奕。

bring down the house　（戲劇演出）成功、轟動

Robin Williams is my favorite comedian. He brings down
the house every time.　Robin Williams 是我最喜歡的喜劇演員。他
每次演出都造成轟動。

bring home the bacon　僅能餬口

He works night and day to bring home the bacon.　他夜以繼
日辛勤工作維持生活。

broke　沒錢；一文不名〔亦可作 dead broke，語氣更強〕

I can't lend you any money because I'm broke, too.　我無法借錢給你，因爲我也囊空如洗。

broke

broken record　反覆講同樣話的人〔原意爲"壞了的唱片"〕

Please stop talking about your problems. You sound like a broken record.　拜託別談你的問題了，你眞像張壞了的唱片。

brown-bag it　野餐〔原意爲"用紙袋裝食品"〕

Let's brown-bag it today. I brought a delicious turkey sand-wich to share.　我們今天就野餐吧！我帶了一個好吃的火雞三明治跟大家--起吃。

brown-nose　拍馬屁

Harold is always brown-nosing the boss.　Harold 總是拍老闆的馬屁。

brown-nose

Brownie points （由額外工作而來的）功勞；表揚

Barb tries to earn Brownie points by staying after school to help the teacher.　Barb 下課後幫助老師以獲得老師的好感。

buck 抗拒

You can't buck the system.　你無法抗拒整個制度。

buck-naked 全裸

He ran buck-naked across the courtyard because somebody stole his underwear.　他內衣被偷，只得裸奔過庭院。

bug off 滾開

Bug off! You're annoying me. 滾開！你真煩人。

bullheaded 頑固；牛脾氣

Terry is so bullheaded;　he won't listen to anybody else's opinion.　Terry 頑固得聽不進別人的意見。

bull headed
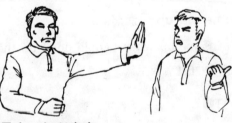

bum around 晃來晃去；無所事事

The kids bummed around all summer.　孩子們整個夏天晃來晃去無所事事。

bum rap 責罵

Louise got a bum rap for taking sides with Richard.　Louise 因為偏袒 Richard 而代為受過遭責罵。

bummer　令人噁心的經驗

That show was a real bummer.　那場表演令人倒盡胃口。

bummer

bundle　一大筆錢

We can make a bundle on this deal.　我們可以在這次交易上大撈一筆。

burn, be burned out（from）　精疲力盡

Janis is burned out from her job.　Janis 工作得累垮了。

burn someone up　激怒...

It burns me up when people don't do their job right.　有人沒把份內的事做好就令我生氣。

burp　打嗝

Don't burp so loud. It's not polite.　不要這麼大聲打嗝，那樣不禮貌。

bush, be bushed（from）　精疲力盡

I'm bushed from working out all afternoon.　我做了一個下午，做得精疲力盡。

butter up　對...說好話

Maybe if we butter up Mother, she'll let us go to the movies.
如果我們對媽說點好聽的，也許她會讓我們去看電影。

butt in　插嘴；打岔　介入·干擾 ↔ butt out

Amy loves to butt in and offer her advice even when it's not
wanted.　不管時機對不對，Amy 都喜歡插嘴提供意見。

butterfingers　容易掉球的人；烏龍選手〔原意爲"手指上有奶油"〕

Bonnie is a real butterfingers when it comes to baseball.
Bonnie 打棒球時常擺烏龍。

butterfingers

**butterflies, have／get butterflies (in one's stomach)
緊張得肚子痛；心裏七上八下**

I always get butterflies when I have to speak in front of the
class.　在全班面前說話時我老是緊張得肚子痛。

button one's lip　住口；閉嘴

Tell Cindy to button her lip or else she'll be in big trouble.
告訴 Cindy 閉嘴，否則她就慘了。

buy time　拖延時間

I think we should try to buy more time.　我想我們應設法拖延時間。

buy　相信；買某人的帳

After Meg finished telling her boss why she was late to work, he said, "I'll buy that."　Meg 告訴老闆她遲到的原因後，他說：「我相信你。」

buzz, give a buzz　打電話

Give me a buzz later on when you get home.　你到家後打電話給我。

call it quits　不幹了

After being in the used car business for 40 years, Harry finally called it quits.　做了四十年中古車業後, Harry 終於洗手不幹了。

call someone's bluff　逼問，揭穿某人之虛偽

When Melissa called his bluff, Jake broke down and told the truth.　Jack 受不了 Melissa 逼問而說了眞話。

call someone's bluff

call the shots　發號施令

Margaret is calling the shots around our house these days. Margaret 這幾天在我們家發號施令。

carry a／the torch for　無怨無悔地愛

She still carries a torch for Vic after all these years. 這些年來她依然無怨無悔地愛著 Vic。

cat gets one's tongue　無言以對〔原意爲"舌頭被貓吃了"〕

Susan was speechless when her boss asked her why she was three hours late for work. Then her boss said, "What's the matter, Susan, cat got your tongue?" 老闆問 Susan 爲何遲到了三小時，她無言以對。老闆說：「怎麼啦？Susan, 你沒話說了吧？」

catch on to　突然了解

It took Cindy a long time to catch on to what Bill was saying. Cindy 許久以後才突然了解 Bill 的話。

catch someone redhanded　當場抓到

They caught the thief redhanded. 他們當場抓到小偷。

catch someone redhanded

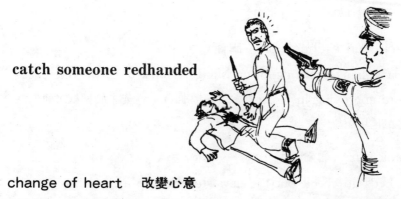

change of heart　改變心意

Edith had originally wanted to be a banker, but she had a change of heart and decided to become a doctor. Edith 原先想當銀行家，後來卻改變心意決定當醫生。

cheap shot　下流手段

The candidates ended up taking cheap shots at each other during the debate.　辯論之中候選人都使用下流手段攻擊對方。

cheap shot

cheapie　便宜貨

It's a cheapie. I spent only a couple of bucks on it.　這是個便宜貨，我才花一兩塊錢買的。

cheapo　小氣鬼；沒格調的人

Brian is a real cheapo. He won't even spend the money to buy his mother a birthday present. Brian 眞是個小氣鬼，他甚至不願意花錢爲他媽媽買生日禮物。

check, run a check on　調查

The bank ran a check on Mr. Davis' list of credit references before approving his loan.　銀行在批准 Davis 先生的貸款之前先調查他的信用記錄。

check out　看看

Let's go check out the new store in the mall. I heard they have some real nice things.　我們去商場那家新開的店看看，聽說他們有一些好東西。

check up on　檢查；核對；探問

I'm going to check up on this last piece of data before submitting my proposal.　在提出計畫前，我要核對這最後一件資料。

Mom called to check up on the kids.　媽打電話來看看孩子是不是都好。

chew somone out　責罵；譴責

Follow the rules and you won't get chewed out.　遵守規定你就不會挨罵。

chicken feed　小錢（＝ peanuts）

I make chicken feed compared to you.　和你比起來，我賺的只是小錢。

chicken out　退縮

Bill was going to ask Lisa out on date, but he chickened out at the last minute.　Bill 本來要約 Lisa 出去玩，但是最後卻不敢開口。

chicken out

chill out　緩和情緒；冷靜下來

Chill out. Things aren't as bad as they seem.　冷靜一點。事情並不像表面上那樣糟。

chip, when the chips are down　事到臨頭

When the chips are down, Marsha is not the person to count on for help.　Marsha 並不是在事到臨頭時可以依靠的人。

when the chips are down

chip in　出錢

We all chipped in to buy Jennifer a going away present. 大家都出錢買一個送別禮物給 Jennifer。

chip, a chip off the old block　一個模子印出來的；酷似（父母的人）

Scott certainly is a chip off the old block. He reminds me so much of his father when he was that age. Scott 像極了他爸爸，讓我想起他爸爸在他這年齡的許多事。

chow down　吃飯

Let's chow down. I'm so hungry.　去吃飯吧，我餓死了。

cinch　必然的事；定局；易如反掌的事

It's a cinch that they'll win the game.　他們會贏已成定局。

clam up　住口；不說話〔原意爲"蚌殼闔起來"〕

When Vinnie entered the room, Mary clammed up.　Vinnie 一進入房間，Mary 就閉嘴了。

鉗,粘.

clamp down on　加強取締，箝制.

The police are clamping down on drunk drivers.　警方加強取締酒後開車。

clamp down on

clean up one's act　洗心革面；重新作人

You'd better clean up your act if you want to go to a good school.　如果你想進好學校就要洗心革面、發憤圖強。

clear up　消除（疑慮、誤會、困難）；弄清楚

We can clear this matter up tomorrow. 明天我們會把這件事弄清楚。

cliffhanger　吊人胃口的東西；懸宕

TV series like *Dallas* usually end the season with a cliffhanger.　像 Dallas 這樣的電視影集經常以吊人胃口的方式結束一季。

clincher　關鍵

The woman's positive identification of the bank robber was the clincher in the court case.　那婦人肯定指認出銀行搶匪，是此案的關鍵。

clip someone's wings　限制；管束

Ralph always stayed out too late, so his father decided to

clip his son's wings. He refused to let Ralph drive the car for a month.　Ralph 總是很晚回家，因此他父親決定要好好管束他，一個月不准他開車。

clock in　打卡

Don't forget to clock in, otherwise you won't get paid.　別忘了打卡，否則領不到錢。

clock in

close, a close shave ∕ call　千鈞一髮

That car almost hit us. What a close shave!　那部車子幾乎撞到我們，差一點就沒命了！

cloud, on cloud nine　飄飄然〔原意為"在九重天上"〕

Daphne was on cloud nine for days after Chip asked her to the prom.　Chip 邀請 Daphne 參加畢業舞會，她興奮了好幾天。

clout　權力；影響力

Mr. Neely has a lot of clout around here.　Neely 先生在這一帶很有影響力。

clout

clue, not have a clue　茫然無緒；莫名其妙

When Steve woke up in a field with his best suit on, he didn't have a clue as to what had happened.　當 Steve 在田裡清醒過來，身上穿著他最好的西裝，他搞不清楚到底發生了什麼事。

cockamamie [kάkəmemɪ]　瘋狂

That is the most cockamamie plan I've ever heard. It will never work.　這是我聽過最瘋狂的計劃，行不通的。

cold, a cold day in hell　不可能的事〔原意為"地獄的冷天"，相傳地獄中永遠是火燒著的，故不可能有冷的時候〕

It will be a cold day in hell before I agree to go out with that jerk Harold.　要我同意和 Harold 那個笨蛋一起出去絕不可能。

cold day in hell

cold feet　緊張；害怕

I get cold feet whenever I have to speak in front of a crowd. 每當我必須在群眾面前說話時，我都會手腳發冷。

cold shoulder　冷落，以冷漠待之

Earl gave Jenny the cold shoulder after finding out that she had dated someone else while he was gone.　Earl 發現 Jenny 在他不在時和別人約會之後，就冷落她。

cold turkey　立即（戒除壞習慣）；二話不說

The best way to stop smoking is to quit cold turkey.　戒煙最好的方法就是說戒就戒。

come across 看起來像；給人感覺是

Paul doesn't come across as a scholar, but he certainly is.
Paul 看起來不像一位學者，可是他的確是。

come after 跟著

The killer came after her with gun. 殺手拿著槍跟在她後面。

I walked away angry, but he came after me to apologize.
我生氣地走開，但他跟過來道歉。

come again 再說一遍

Come again? I didn't quite understand what you said. 再說一
遍，你剛說的話我不了解。

come clean 全盤托出，招供

The criminal decided to come clean. 罪犯決定供出事實。

come down hard on 以嚴厲態度對待；和...算帳

If you don't work diligently, the boss will come down hard
on you. 如果你不努力工作，老闆會找你算帳。

come down with 生（病）

I came down with a bad cold last week. 上星期我得了重感冒。

come easily 易如反掌［原意為“來得容易”］

Languages come easily to some people. 有些人學習語言易如反
掌。

come on to 對...輕薄；吃豆腐

Tanya slapped Bill after he came on to her. Tanya 在 Bill
吃她豆腐之後打他一巴掌。

come up with　想出（好主意）

Michael came up with a brand-new plan in just a few minutes.　Michael 很快想出了一個好計劃。

come up with

come with the territory　免不了的

You have to expect some problems along the way. It comes with the territory.　你最好對接下去可能發生的問題有心理準備，這是免不了的。

comeback　敏捷機智的反擊（反駁）

John can always think of a good comeback whenever someone teases him. 每當有人消遣他時，John 總是能想出巧妙的反擊。

conk out　①不醒人事〔睡着或昏倒〕②壞了

① An hour after she fainted, she woke up and asked the doctor, "How did I conk out?"　她昏倒一個小時後醒過來，問醫生說：「我是怎麼失去知覺的？」

② The refrigerator finally conked out.　冰箱終於壞了。

cook up　想出

He cooked up a wonderful way to surprise his wife on her birthday.　他想出一個在他太太生日時讓她驚喜的妙法。

cool　帥；瀟灑

He's so cool. All the girls want to go out with him.　他真瀟灑，所有的女生都想跟他出去。

cool it　冷靜一點

Cool it. You're making me mad.　冷靜一點，你快把我逼瘋了。

cop-out　溜走

Don't cop-out on me now. You promised you'd go.　別想溜，你說你會去的。

copycat　跟屁蟲

I hate it when Linda tries to imitate everything I do. She's such a copycat.　我討厭 Linda 每件事模仿我，她真是個跟屁蟲。

copycat

corny　陳腔濫調；了無新意

Fred's jokes are always so corny.　Fred的笑話總是了無新意。

couch potato　整天看電視的人　［原意為"沙發上的馬鈴薯"］

Jane is definitely a couch potato. She snacks in front of the TV all day.　Jane 真是個電視迷，她整天都窩在電視前面吃零食。

couch potato

cough it up　（不情願地）付錢

Cough it up. I know you have the twenty dollars.　付錢吧！
我知道你有這二十元的。

could not care less　無所謂；不在乎

I couldn't care less if you ask her out or not.　你邀不邀她出
去，我一點也不在乎。

cover for　掩護；罩

Don't worry about Mother, I'll cover for you this time.　別擔
心媽媽那邊，這一次我會罩你。

crack up　爆笑出來

Joey told a funny story and we all cracked up.　Joey 說了一
個笑話，我們都爆笑出來。

cranky　脾氣暴躁

Grandpa is really cranky if he doesn't have his afternoon
nap.　祖父如果不睡午覺就會很暴躁。

crazy about　爲...痴狂；瘋狂喜歡

He's crazy about the new girl in class.　他爲班上新來的那個女
生痴狂。

crazy about

creepy　恐怖的

That was a creepy movie. I'll probably have nightmares tonight.　那是一部恐怖片，今晚我也許會做惡夢。

crib card／sheet　小抄

Paul tried to cheat on his test by sneaking in a crib card. Paul 想夾帶小抄作弊。

cross a bridge when／before one comes to it　船到橋頭自然直

Stop worrying about your piano recital. You'll cross that bridge when you come to it.　別擔心你的鋼琴獨奏會，船到橋頭自然直。

cruise　兜風

Let's go cruising the streets of downtown in my new sports car.　坐我的新跑車到市區兜風吧！

cruise

crummy　很爛的；很菜的

What a crummy restaurant! The plates were dirty and the food was awful. 這家餐廳眞爛！盤子髒，菜又差！

D

cut a deal　達成協議

I think we should cut a deal before they sign with another company.　我想我們應該在他們與另一家公司簽約之前達成協議。

cut it out　住手；停止

Cut it out! I don't have time to start a fight with you. 住口！我沒時間和你吵！

darn　混帳

Darn! I missed the bus. Now I'll have to wait another twenty minutes.　混帳！我錯過了那班車，又要等二十分鐘。

darn

day in court　申訴的機會

When Mr. Jones was explaining what had happened, Mr. Smith was silent. He knew he would get his day in court.　Jones 先生解釋所發生的事時，Smith 先生沈默不語，後者知道他會有機會申辯的。

dead ahead　正前方

The school is dead ahead about 2 miles from here.　學校在正前二哩處。

dead giveaway　肯定的事實

Jill's runny nose and watery eyes were a dead giveaway that she was coming down with a cold.　Jill 鼻涕眼淚直流，她一定感冒了。

deal someone in　讓...參加

Deal me in. I want to play too. 讓我參加，我也要玩。

deal someone in

deep, in deep trouble　有麻煩

You better behave yourself or else you'll be in deep trouble when Mom gets home.　你最好乖一點，否則媽一回來你就慘了。

dibs　權利

He gets first dibs because he's the oldest.　他年紀最大，所以有優先權。

diddly squat　微不足道的報酬

He gave me diddly squat for all my hard work. See if I ever help him again.　他給我這一點微不足道的報酬，看我以後會不會再幫他。

die for　好得值得爲之付出生命

Jason is to die for. I'd do anything to go out with him.
Jason 眞棒，我願意做任何事來換得和他出去。

dingbat　笨蛋，白痴

What a dingbat! Marjorie is always doing stupid things.
Marjorie 眞是個白痴，總是做傻事。

dip　傻瓜

Ben can be such a dip at times. He often says the wrong
thing at the wrong time.　Ben 有時候眞笨，他常在不對的時間說不
對的話。

dirty work　爛攤子

It's not fair! I always have to do your dirty work while you
take all the credit.　這不公平！我一天到晚爲你收拾爛攤子，功勞卻
全是你的。

do a number on　欺負；作手脚

He really did a number on you. Why did you let him take
advantage of you like that?　他眞是欺你太甚，你爲什麼讓他這樣佔
你便宜呢？

don't have a cow　別大驚小怪！

Don't have a cow! I'll pay for the damages.　別大驚小怪！我
會賠償損失。

do-hickey　不知道名字的小玩意

This do-hickey here, what do you call it?　這個小玩意兒，你
管它叫什麼？

don't knock it　不要太挑剔

Don't knock it! You won't be able to find another job that pays so well.　別挑剔了！你未必可以找到另一個待遇這麼好的工作！

don't knock it

dorky　傻乎乎的

Jesse looks so dorky with his new haircut and glasses. Jesse 剛剪頭髮戴上新眼鏡的樣子看起來傻乎乎的。

do time　坐牢；服刑

Marvin is doing time for robbing the bank.　Marvin 在爲搶銀行坐牢。

dough　錢〔原意爲"麵團"〕

Can you lend me some dough？I don't get paid until next Friday.　能不能借我一些錢？我下星期五才發薪。

√ down and out　貧困潦倒

Sarah was down and out after losing her job and her apartment.　Sarah 失去職業和房子之後變得貧困潦倒。

down in the dumps　垂頭喪氣；意志消沈

The players were down in the dumps after their team lost the championship game.　球員輸掉冠軍爭奪戰之後個個垂頭喪氣。

down to the wire　等到最後一刻才開始做事

Peter always waits until the last minute to do his work. I could never leave it down to the wire like that.　Peter 總是等到最後一刻才開始做事，我從不像他那樣火燒屁股。

drag　討厭

What a drag! There's nothing to do here.　眞討厭！這裏什麼都沒得混！

drive someone up the wall　把人逼瘋、逼急

You're driving me up the wall with all your whining and complaining.　你的哭訴快把我逼瘋了。

drop, a drop in the bucket　滄海一粟

The amount of money Mr. Howell spent on a new Rolls-Royce was just a drop in the bucket compared to his annual salary.　Howell 先生買一部新 Rolls Royce 的錢和他的年薪相比只不過是滄海一粟。

drop dead　去死！

Suzy told Mike, "Drop dead!" when he kept teasing her about her weight.　Mike 不停地消遣 Suzy 的體重，Suzy 說「你去死！」。

drop in／by／over　隨時造訪

Feel free to drop in anytime. I'm usually home and I'd love the company.　歡迎隨時來坐，我通常在家，也喜歡有人作伴。

drop out　輟學，不唸書〔亦常作 " high-school dropout "（自中學就輟學在外面混的人）〕

Greg dropped out of high school and joined a street gang. Greg 高中不唸了，加入了街上的幫派。

drown one's sorrows　藉酒消愁

After Megan dumped Chuck, Chuck went to the bar to drown his sorrows over a beer.　自從 Megan 甩了 Chuck 後，Chuck 到酒吧喝啤酒消愁。

drown one's sorrows

duck　閃躲；突然低下頭

Remind little Bobby to duck his head when he crawls under the table so he won't hit his head.　提醒 Booby 爬到桌下時要低頭才不會受傷。

dud　不中用的東西

This tape recorder is a dud. It won't play my cassette.　這架錄音機壞了，不能放我的錄音帶。

dude　傢伙；穿戴講究的公子哥兒

Hey dude! What's up?　嘿，老哥！什麼事啊？

E

ear, keep an ear to the ground　注意事態發展或人們的反應

The city manager kept an ear to the ground for a while before deciding to raise city employees' pay.　市府祕書在決定提高市府員工薪資之前曾聽取各方意見好一陣子。

earful, an earful of　滔滔不絕地說

He gave me an earful of complaints about his new boss.　他滔滔不絕向我抱怨他的新老闆。

early bird　早起的人

Mary is an early bird. She gets up around five o'clock every morning.　Mary 是個早起的人，她每天大約五點鐘起床。

elbow grease　力量

You need to use more elbow grease when waxing the car. I can't see my reflection on the hood yet.　你給汽車上蠟時要多用點力，我在引擎蓋上還看不出我的倒影。

elevator music　電梯間或電話中"稍待"時所播放的音樂

I wish they wouldn't play elevator music when they put you on hold.　但願你等對方接聽電話時不會讓你老聽那"稍待"音樂。

even-steven　公平的

To be fair, we'll split this piece of candy even-steven.　為了公平起見，我們均分這塊糖。

eye-opener　令人大開眼界的事

Listening to him talk about his adventures in China was a

real eye-opener　聽他談在中國的驚險故事令人大開眼界。

eye-opener

face up to　面對現實

The boy knew he should tell his neighbor that he broke the window, but he just couldn't face up to it.　男孩知道他該告訴鄰居他打破了窗子，但是他就是不敢面對現實。

√ **fair shake　公平的待遇**

I don't think I got a fair shake in the interview. He made up his mind from the start that he didn't like me.　我認爲我在面試受到不公平的待遇，他一開始就不喜歡我。

fake it　假裝

When you don't understand what he's saying, just fake it by nodding and smiling a lot.　你不知道他在說什麼時，只要點頭裝懂多笑一點就好了。

fake it

F

fake someone out　騙過

The quarterback faked the other team out by keeping the ball instead of passing it.　四分衛持球不傳，騙過了敵隊。

fall flat　失敗；碰壁；未達預期效果

The outdoor swimming party fell flat because of the rain. 室外游泳會因雨而無法舉行。

His joke fell flat because no one understood it.　他的笑話沒人聽懂，所以沒有收到效果。

fall for　上當

We played a trick on him and he fell for it.　我們捉弄他，他上當了。

fall for

fancy-schmancy　[ʃmænsɪ]　豪華的

They live in a fancy-schmancy house in the richest neighborhood.　他們住在高級住宅區的豪華宅第。

far out　①很棒　②奇怪的

① That is a really far out hairdo.　Where'd you get it done? 怪棒的髮型，你在哪裡做的！

② This theory is too far out for me.　這個理論對我來說是太玄了。

fast, life in the fast lane　刺激的生活 [fast lane 快車道]

Jane likes to live life in the fast lane. Wherever there's a party, she is sure to be there.　Jane 喜歡過刺激興奮的生活，哪兒有宴會，她就去那兒。

fed up　受夠了

I'm fed up with your insults and complaints. I quit!　我受夠了你的侮辱和怨氣，我不幹了！

feel someone out　探聽...意向

John asked Dave to feel Jane out about whether she'd be interested in going out with him.　John 要求 Dave 探聽是否 Jane 有興趣和他出去。

feel someone out

fiddle around　玩弄

Don't fiddle around with the television set. You'll end up breaking it.　不要玩電視機。你會弄壞的。

✓ fill someone in on　告知（錯過的事情）

I missed the meeting. Could you please fill me in on what happened?　我錯過了這次聚會。請你告訴我發生了什麼事，好嗎？

✓ fishy　可疑的

His story sounds fishy. We should see if it's really true.　他

的故事聽起來很可疑，我們應該看看到底是不是真的。

fishy

fit (the description) to a T　完全符合描述

The police were looking for a man who was 6'2" with brown hair, blue eyes and a pineapple tattooed on his cheek.　The man in Mr. Brown's store fit the description to a T, so he called the police.　警方正在尋找一個身高六呎二吋，棕髮藍眼，臉頰上有鳳梨刺青的人。布朗先生店裡有個人完全符合這些描述，於是他就打電話給警方。

**fit the description
to a 'T'**

fix someone up　　撮合

I think Beth and Craig would make a perfect couple. Let's fix them up.　我想 Beth 和 Craig 會是理想的一對，我們來撮合他們吧！

flip out　樂死了

Chris flipped out when I told him that he made the basketball team.　我告訴 Chris 被選上籃球隊時，他樂歪了。

flop　（表演電影等）不賣座、失敗

The movie was a flop.　Nobody went to see it.　這部電影賣座奇慘，沒有人去看。

fluke, by a fluke　僥倖

She won the writing contest by a fluke.　She had only spent 20 minutes writing her essay.　她僥倖贏了作文比賽，她寫那篇文章才花了二十分鐘。

fly off the handle　發脾氣

There's no need to fly off the handle. We can discuss this rationally.　沒有必要發脾氣，我們可以理性地討論。

fly off the handle

fly the coop　脫離（監禁）

May's parents were sad because she was flying the coop to go off to college.　May 的父母很傷心因她擺脫家庭去上大學了。

✓ follow through on　遵守（諾言）

It's important that you follow through on your promises,

otherwise nobody will trust you. 你要遵守你的諾言,否則沒有人會信任你。

fool around　鬼混;遊手好閒;不務正業

We fooled around until midnight and then we started on our homework. 我們一直鬼混到深夜才開始寫作業。

for crying out loud　[驚訝的感嘆]

For crying out loud, haven't you finished that book yet? 哎喲,你還沒有看完那本書嗎?

forget it　算了 [生氣的語調]

Forget it! I'll do it myself. 算了!我自己做。

for openers　首先

For openers, we need to design invitations for the wedding. 首先,我們必須設計結婚請帖。

for openers

foul up　破壞

The telephone lines are fouled up, so I can't make my phone call. 電話線被破壞了,我不能打電話。

freak out   緊張；嚇死

Don't freak out. It's only a little field mouse.   別緊張，只不過是一隻小老鼠而已。

freebie   免費招待的

Since John was the hundredth customer, he was given a freebie lunch.   John 是第一百位顧客，所以餐廳招待他一頓免費午餐。

freeloader   利用別人慷慨佔便宜的人

Zach is a real freeloader. He's been staying with Steve and eating all his food.   Zach 真是一個愛占便宜的人，他一直住在 Steve 家裡白吃白喝。

from scratch   從頭開始

Patty made a cake from scratch. It was much better than the cakes I make from a mix.   Patty 從頭開始做蛋糕，比我用現成調好的材料做的好得多。

fudge!   ①糟了！②瞎扯

① Fudge! I forgot to buy Jenny a birthday present.   糟了！我忘了買 Jenny 的生日禮物。

② If you don't know the answer, just fudge it.   如果你不知道答案，就瞎扯一下。

funky   蠻特別的

We listened to some funky music.   我們聽了一些蠻特別的音樂。

G

gag me with a spoon　我快吐了

Gag me with a spoon!　Please don't tell me such disgusting stories anymore.　我快吐了！請別再說這些噁心的故事了。

gawk　呆看

After the plane crashed, there were hundreds of people standing around gawking.　飛機墜落後，好幾百人站在那裡呆呆地看著。

gee whiz　天啊

Gee whiz! Can't you do anything by yourself？　天啊！你難道自己一點事都不會做？

get a clue　了解

Why do you always ask so many questions?　Get a clue! 為什麼你老是問這麼多問題？自己想想看嘛！

get a grip on　控制（脾氣、個性）

Get a grip on it.　You have to be strong in front of the others.　控制一下，你在別人面前要堅強些。

get a kick out of　從...得到極大樂趣；感到過癮

I get a kick out of watching the baby dance.　我看小孩跳舞就高興。

get a load of　（注意）看！

Get a load of this; the circus is coming to town.　看！馬戲團進城了。

get a move on 趕快

Get a move on; you can't park your car here. 趕快，你不能在這裡停車。

get a move on

get after 盯著；責備

Ann's mother gets after her to hang up her clothes. Ann 的媽媽盯著她把衣服掛好。

Bob's father gets after him for tracking mud into the house. Bob 把泥巴踩進屋裡被父親責罵。

get away with 逃過懲罰；逍遙法外

Some students can get away with not doing their homework because they are so smart. 有些學生可以不作功課也沒有事，因為他們太聰明了。

get away with

get away with murder　做壞事而不受處罰

Mrs. Jones lets her children get away with murder. Jones 太太縱容小孩做壞事。

∨ get one's feet wet　參與；開始做

It's not good to concentrate all your efforts on just writing. You should get your feet wet and try painting or dancing. 單單寫作對你不好，你應該涉獵一下繪畫和舞蹈。

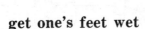

get one's feet wet

get going　離開

I have to get going. It's late and they're expecting me for dinner. 我得走了，時候已不早了，他們在等我吃晚飯。

get in someone's hair　煩，惹 [相反的片語是 stay out of someone's hair]

Don't get in his hair. He doesn't like to be bothered when he's working. 別去煩他，他不喜歡工作時被人打擾。

get lost　滾開

A stray cat was lurking outside the fish market and the

owner yelled at it, "Get lost!" 一隻野貓在魚市場前探頭探腦，魚販對它大叫「滾開」。

get off someone's back 不打擾；讓人清靜

Christy told Todd to get off her back so she could finish her paper. Christy 告訴 Todd 別打擾她，讓她把報告寫完。

get off someone's back

get on someone's nerves 讓人氣惱

Jack's annoying habits really gets on my nerves at times. Jack 討厭的習慣有時真讓我氣惱。

get on the ball 用心做

If you hope to keep your job, you'd better get on the ball and meet the deadline. 如果你還想要你的工作，你最好用心做，不要拖泥帶水。

get over 自...中恢復過來

I don't think anybody really gets over his first love. 我認為沒有人能夠真正忘掉他的初戀。

get the drift   了解

Stop me when you get the drift. I don't want to bore you with something you already understand. 你聽懂了就叫停，我不想重複你已經知道的事。

get the drift

get the hang of   進入情況；抓到竅門

I think if I practice serving a couple of times, I'll get the hang of it. 我想如果我多練習發幾次球，我就會抓到竅門了。

get the picture   了解

Two's company, three's a crowd. Get the picture?   二人成行，三人成伍，懂了嗎？

get through to   讓（人）了解到

When the rich boy's father lost his fortune, it took a long time for the idea to get through to the boy that he would have to work and support himself. 男孩的富有父親破產好久以後，男孩才逐漸明白他必須工作養活自己。

I'm not getting through to you, am I?   你不了解我的意思，對不對？

get with it 留意（周遭的事物）

George really needs to get with it. He's still wearing bell-bottoms. George 真的該留意一下時尚，他仍然穿著喇叭褲。

get with it ①用功；努力 ②使自己跟得上時代

① I got really low marks on my first three tests; my teacher told me to get with it or I'm going to get a 'D' for the course. 我前三次考得極差，老師叫我用功點，否則那科就要給我一個丁。

② Why are you still listening to Michael Jackson? He was famous last year, but this year he's not cool. C'mon, get with it!

你為什麼還在聽 Michael Jackson？ 他去年很紅，但今年不行了。好啦！要跟得上時代!

give it a shot ／ whirl 試試看

Joan had never skied before, but she decided to give it a shot. Joan 從沒有滑過雪，但她決定試試看。

give it a shot (whirl)

give someone a hard time 跟某人過不去

Ed loves to give his sister a hard time, just to make her mad. Ed 愛和他姊姊過不去，故意叫她生氣。

give someone a ring　給...打電話

I'll give you a ring when I get in town.　我到城裡會打電話給你。

give out　癱掉了

His legs gave out just as he crossed the finish line of the 20k marathon.　他一跑過 20 公里馬拉松的終點線以後，腿就癱掉了。

go-ahead　可以開始做的指示

Sheila gave him the go-ahead to start his new assignment. Sheila 告訴他可以開始做新的工作了。

go all out　盡力而為；全力以赴

Terry went all out with the Christmas decorations.　Terry 全副精神都花在耶誕裝飾上。

I intend to go all out to make them comfortable.　我會盡一切力量讓他們舒服。

go along with　支持；參與

I'll go along with your plan, as long as you're sure it will work.　我會支持你的計劃，只要你確定會有用。

go along with

go Dutch　各付各的

I insist that we go Dutch.　You shouldn't have to pay for my

share. 我堅持各付各的，你用不著付我的份。

go fly a kite　滾蛋

Jenny told Greg to go fly a kite after he told her he had to break their date.　Greg 告訴 Jenny 必須取消他們的約會後，Jenny 叫他滾蛋。

go for it　去做（冒險的事）

I think you should go for it.　What have you got to lose? 我認為你該試試看。你又會損失什麼呢!?

go off the deep end　鋌而走險；做出意想不到之事［過度的情緒反應］。

Ann is so depressed I hope she doesn't go off the deep end. Ann 這麼消沈，我希望她不要做出傻事。

go off the deep end

goner　無可救藥的人

Mark's a goner.　He didn't finish his chores before going out.　Mark 眞無可救藥，他工作沒做完就走掉了。

goody-two-shoes　天眞爛漫［諷刺性語氣］

Pamela is such a goody-two-shoes.　She's always so sweet and innocent in front of the grown-ups.　Pamela 眞是天眞爛漫哪！她總是在大人面前顯得甜美純潔。

goof around ／ off　無所事事；遊蕩

During the summer, kids get to goof around because there is no school.　夏天孩子們不必上學而得以四處遊蕩。

goof up　犯錯，出岔子

Don't goof up.　This project is too important.　別出岔子，這個計劃非常重要。

go overboard　做得過頭了

Sandy went overboard when she planned this party.　There's enough food here to feed twice as many people.　Sandy 計劃宴會時設想太過周到，準備的東西足夠給兩倍的人吃。

go places　有辦法

Paul's really going places.　In just two short·months of working here, he has already been promoted.　Paul 眞有辦法。才工作兩個月就升職了。

go public　公開宣布

Mr. Smith went public today that he was retiring. Smith 先生今天公開宣布他要退休了。

go public

go up in smoke　成爲泡影

Peter's vacation plans went up in smoke when a crisis arose in the office.　辦公室出了問題，Peter 的假期也泡湯了。

go up in smoke

go with the flow　隨從大家的意見

Sharon is an easy going person. She just goes with the flow. Sharon 是個隨和的人，人家怎麼做，她就怎麼做。

✓ grade, make the grade　稱職；合乎水準、要求

Susan was worried about making the grade in her new executive position.　Susan 擔心不知自己能否勝任新的主管職務。

If you don't make the grade, you can't be a member of the club.　如果你不合格，就不能成爲俱樂部的一員。

green thumb　園藝天才

He certainly has a green thumb. All his plants flourish.　他眞有園藝天才，種的植物都生意盎然。

gross　噁心

Don't chew with your mouth open. It is really gross.　別張口大嚼，眞噁心。

gross someone out　讓人覺得噁心

Mike grossed Sue out when he waved a snake in front of her face.　Mike 在 Sue 面前搖一條蛇，使她噁心死了。

grossed out

groupie　一群影迷；歌迷

Ever since John attained stardom, he's had groupies follow him everywhere he goes.　自從 John 成爲明星之後，到那裡都有一群人跟著他。

guest, be my guest　請便

When Laura asked if she could borrow his bicycle, Bob said, "Be my guest."　Laura 問 Bob 能否借用他的脚踏車時，Bob 說，〔請便。〕

gung-ho　熱衷，興致勃勃

Ted is really gung-ho about the new project.　Ted 對新計劃興致勃勃。

gung ho

half-baked　膚淺的；半調子

How do you come up with all these half-baked ideas ? You should think them out more carefully.　你怎麼會想出這些膚淺的主意的？　你應該仔細地考慮考慮。

hands down　易如反掌；輕鬆

Jason didn't put in his full effort and he still won hands down.　Jason 並未盡全力，卻也輕鬆獲勝。

hands down

hands-off　無爲而治；順其自然

He takes a hand-off approach when it comes to raising his children. He leaves all the decisions up to his wife.　他用無爲而治的方式教養小孩，一切事情都由太太決定。

hands-on experience　親手獲得的經驗；第一手經驗

Jill thought her hands-on experience as editor of her school newspaper was what got her the reporting job at the local newspaper.　Jill 認爲她在學校報紙擔任編輯的第一手經驗，使她得到了地方報紙的記者工作。

H

hang around　溜達；等待以排遣時間

I get off work in 15 minutes.　If you don't mind hanging around, we can go out to get a bite to eat.　我還有十五分鐘才下班，如果你不介意稍等一下，我們可以一道去吃點東西。

hang in there　忍耐一下

Hang in there. Things will look up soon.　忍耐一下，事情很快會有好轉的。

hang out　溜達

In her free time, Kathy likes to hang out at the mall with her frineds.　Kathy 有空喜歡和朋友到商場溜達。

hard, be hard on　①對...嚴格　②使...費勁

① Some fathers are very hard on their children.　有些父親對小孩子非常嚴格。

② Making a lot of speeches can be hard on your voice.　演講太多會讓你的嗓子受不了。

has-been　過氣的人

Lisa is a has-been.　Nobody will hire her anymore.　Lisa 已經過氣了，沒有人會再僱用她。

hassle　麻煩的事物；招惹；煩

I won't do it because it's too much of a hassle.　這事情太麻煩，我不想碰。

Don't hassle me.　別煩我！

have a ball　尋樂，痛快地玩

We intend to have a ball at the amusement park today.　我們打算今天痛快地到遊樂場玩一玩。

have a bone to pick with　〝有帳要算〞

I have a bone to pick with you. You still owe me the fifteen dollars you borrowed.　我有帳跟你算，你向我借的十五元還沒還呢！

**have a bone
to pick with**

have a chip on one's shoulder　情緒不佳；暴躁

Valerie certainly has a chip on her shoulder. Why is she so touchy?　Valerie 顯然情緒不佳，她為什麼這麼暴躁？

have a field day　縱情放任；為所欲為

The press is having a field day with the kidnapping of the mayor's daughter.　報紙大肆渲染市長女兒被綁架的消息。

have, do not have a prayer　沒指望

Our team doesn't have a prayer today. They're playing the number one team in the league.　我們這一隊今天沒指望了，他們將和聯盟的冠軍隊打。

have had it　受夠了

I've had it with all your excuses.　我受夠了你的藉口。

have it bad for　狂戀

He really has it bad for her, but she has no idea.　他狂戀著她，她卻不知道。

have it bad for

have it good　享受得很

She really has it good. Everybody caters to her every need. 她真是享受得很，要什麼就有什麼。

have it in for　對...生氣

He really has it in for you. What did you do to provoke him?　他對你非常生氣，你惹到他什麼了？

hit　熱門

You're a hit! The audience loved your performance.　你真是個大熱門！觀眾喜歡你的表演。

hit someone with a problem　讓...面對問題

I'm sorry to hit you with this problem. I don't know who else to turn to.　很抱歉把這個問題扔給你，我不知道還有誰可以找。

hit it off　投緣；一見如故

They hit it off instantly and have been good friends ever since.　他們一見面就很投緣，從此就成了好朋友。

hit the ceiling　氣瘋了

When dad got the estimate for fixing the car, he hit the ceiling. He had no idea it would be so expensive.　爸爸拿到修車估價單時氣瘋了，他沒想到會這麼貴。

hit the ceiling

hit the hay／sack　睡覺

I'm going to hit the hay. It's been a long day and I'm exhausted.　我要去睡覺了，從早忙到晚我累壞了。

hit the road　上路

We should probably hit the road. It's going to take us two hours to get home.　我們該上路了吧！回到家要兩個小時哦！

hog, go whole hog　全力以赴

She went whole hog in planning her New Year's Eve party. 她全心全力籌辦除夕晚會。

horse around　嬉鬧

We've horsed around long enough. It's time to get to work. 我們鬧夠了，該工作了。

hot stuff　大人物

He thinks he's hot stuff, but everybody else thinks he's a jerk.　他自以爲了不得，其他人卻把他看做傻瓜。

hot stuff

hot under the collar　非常生氣

He's still hot under the collar about the trick we played on him.　他還在氣我們對他開的玩笑。

hung over　宿醉未醒

Don't disturb Steve. He's still hung over from last night.　不要吵 Steve，他宿醉仍未醒。

hang up on　掛電話

I can't believe she hung up on me after putting me on hold for ten minutes.　我眞不敢相信她竟然在讓我等了十分鐘之後把電話掛斷了。

hunky-dory　沒問題

Everything here is hunky-dory. Don't worry.　這裡一切沒問題，別擔心。

I kid you not　我不騙你

I kid you not. I saw this woman talking to her hand.　我不騙你，我看見這個女人跟她的手說話。

I kid you not

icky　因太過甜膩而難吃

This cake tastes icky. Do I have to eat it?　這蛋糕太甜了，我一定得吃嗎？

in　流行〔相反詞為 “out” （落伍了）〕

You're the fashion expert. Are long or short skirts in this year?　你是流行專家，今年流行長裙還是短裙？

in a bind　有困難

Next time you're in a bind, let me know and I'll be glad to help.　下次你有困難要讓我知道，我會樂意幫你忙的。

in hot water　有麻煩

Joe's in hot water with the boss because he's been late three times this week.　Joe 在老闆那裡有麻煩了，因為這個禮拜他遲到了三次。

in the bag　志在必得；囊中物

This game is in the bag. There's no way we can lose.　這場

比賽我們志在必得，怎麼都不會輸的。

in the bag

in the cards   意料中事

It's in the cards that Joy and Steve will get married soon.
Joy 和 Steve 很快就會結婚是意料中事。

in the doghouse   被冷藏、打入冷宮

Dan is in the doghouse for missing his curfew.   Dan 因為違反宵禁而被冷藏。

in the driver's seat   掌握大權

Tom is in the driver's seat. He makes all the decisions.
Tom 掌握大權，他做所有的決定。

in the driver's seat

iron out the kinks 解決小問題 [原意爲 "熨平小皺紋"]

The contract will be ready to sign as soon as we iron out a few of the kinks. 我們把一些小問題解決之後就可以簽合約了。

It's been real 很高興遇見你！[來自 " It's been real nice to meet you." 常意帶嘲諷]

It's been real. I hope we can get together again very soon. 很高興遇見你。我希望我們能很快再聚會。

jazz, all that jazz 諸如此類

He only cares about baseball, TV, girls, and all that jazz. 他只關心籃球、電視、女孩這一類事情。

jerk 笨蛋 [含"沒有見過世面"之意]

Fred is a real jerk. He's rude and obnoxious. Fred 眞是個笨蛋，他粗魯又惹人厭。

john 廁所

I have to go to the john. Wait for me in the car. 我要上一號，在車裡等我一下。

John Hancock

John Hancock 簽名

Put your John Hancock right here. 請在這裡簽名。

joy ride　兜風

We went for a joy ride in Tim's new Corvette.　我們坐 Tim 新的 Corvette 車去兜風。

jump the gun　草率行事

Don't jump the gun. We have to be patient for a while.　不要草率行事，我們應耐心等一會兒。

junkie　吸毒者

The junkie stole some money in order to buy more drugs. 吸毒者爲了買更多的毒品而偷錢。

junkie

keep in line　管束

He needs to be kept in line. He's too wild.　他太野了要好好管束。

keep in line

keep it under wraps 保密

Don't tell anyone about the party. Let's just keep it under wraps. 不要把舞會告訴任何人，這件事不要洩露出去。

keep one's shirt on 保持冷靜

Keep your shirt on. He didn't mean to offend you. That's just the way he talks. 保持冷靜，那只是他說話的樣子，他並非有意要觸怒你。

keep up with the Joneses 和鄰人別苗頭

To keep up with the Joneses, Mrs. Smith bought a Ming vase that was bigger and more expensive than theirs. 爲了和鄰居別苗頭，Smith 太太買了一個比他們的更大更貴的明朝花瓶。

**keep up with the
Joneses**

kick around 討論；多作考慮

Let's kick around a few more proposals before we come to a final decision. 我們作最後決定之前多考慮幾個方案吧！

kick in 出（錢）

If everybody kicks in five dollars, we can buy a nice Christmas present for the secretary. 如果每個人出五塊錢，我們就可以買很好的聖誕禮物給祕書。

klutz　呆瓜；傻瓜

He's such a klutz.　他真是個傻瓜。

knock it off（＝ cut if off）　停止

Knock it off! I'm trying to get some sleep.　別吵了！我正設法睡覺呢！

knock someone out　讓人樂死了

She knocked her friends out with the delicious meal she spent all day preparing.　她準備了一天的豐盛大餐，讓她的朋友吃得大呼過癮。

know-it-all　萬事通

Grace is always correcting other people. She thinks she's a know-it-all.　Grace 總是在糾正別人，她覺得自己是萬事通。

know-it-all

knucklehead　傻瓜

You knucklehead! Can't you do anything right?　你這傻瓜！你不能做對一件事嗎？

kooky　古怪的

That man is really kooky. He has fifty-three cats！　那個人眞怪，他養了五十三隻貓！

lady-killer　帥哥

He's a real lady-killer.　他眞是個帥哥。

laid back　隨和的；輕鬆的

I really like Kathy. She's laid back and easy to get along with.　我眞喜歡 Kathy，她隨和、好相處。

lay off　停止；解雇

Lay off! I don't need you to tell me what to do.　別再唸了！我不需要你告訴我怎麼做！

leg, have a hollow leg　胃口奇大；怎麼吃都吃不飽

The way Gary eats, you would think he has a hollow leg. 看 Gary 的吃相，你會以爲他怎麼吃都吃不飽。

have a hollow leg

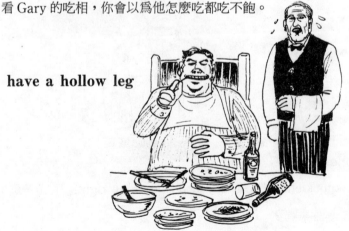

leg, a leg up 占上風

All Jeff's hard work is paying off. He's a leg up on the rest of his competitors.　Jeff 的努力是有代價的，他在競爭對手中占了上風。

lemon 爛貨〔指"全新的東西却不斷出毛病"〕

This car is a real lemon. I've had it for only a year and already it's broken down four times.　這部車子眞爛，我才買了一年就壞了四次。

lemon

let someone have it 讓...好看

Next time I see Rick, I'm going to let him have it.　下次我看到 Rick 時要他好看。

let's get this show on the road 開始做事

That's enough socializing; let's get this show on the road. Or else, we'll be here all night.　交際夠了，辦一點正事吧！不然，我們要整晚都待在這裡了。

let the cat out of the bag　洩露祕密；"大嘴巴"

Janie let the cat out of the bag when she told everybody Henry's secret.　Janie 眞是個大嘴巴，她到處說 Henry 的祕密。

low-life　落魄潦倒的人

Chris is such a low-life. He sleeps on the park bench and drink booze all day.　Chris 眞是落魄潦倒，他睡在公園板橙上整天喝酒。

luck out　走狗運；走霉運〔有正反兩種用法〕

She really lucked out this time. She didn't get caught coming home late.　算她這次走狗運，晚回家沒被逮到。

lunch, out to lunch　神經病；神智不清

Richard stands on his head in the shower. He's really out to lunch.　Richard 在浴室倒立，他眞是有病。

out to lunch

make a federal case out of　誇大；小題大作

Don't make a federal case out of it!　You can barely tell that there is a scratch on your car.　別小題大作！你的車子看不出有任何刮痕。

make a killing　大有斬獲

He made a killing on that deal. I wish I had bought some shares.　他在那筆生意上大有斬獲，眞希望當初我也加入了。

make a mountain out of a molehill　小題大作

I'm tired of listening to John make a mountain out of a mole-hill. He constantly complains about minor things.　我受不了 John 小題大作，他不斷抱怨一些不重要的事。

make a mountain out of a molehill

✓ make a scene　出糗；出洋相

Don't make a scene! We'll discuss this when we get home. 別在這裡出糗，這問題我們回家再談。

✓ make my day　使我高興；讓我很 "爽"

Thanks for the good news. You've made my day.　謝謝你的好消息，你讓我覺得很爽。

✓ make waves　興風作浪 ；引起軒然大波

If my sister finds out about this, she's really going to make waves.　假如我妹妹發現這件事，她必定會興風作浪。

market, in the market for　想買；積極物色

People are always in the market for something new and different.　人們總想買點新奇的東西。

in the market for

meddle in　干涉；攪和

Harold asked his boss to stop meddling in his personal life. Harold 要求老闆別再干涉他的私生活。

mess around　廝混

We'd better stop messing around. The teacher's coming.　我們最好別再混了，老師來了。

mind, to give a piece of one's mind　責備

Sarah gave her husband a piece of her mind when he came home drunk two nights in a row.　Sarah 罵她先生，因爲他連續兩夜喝醉回家。

**give a piece of
one's mind**

miss the boat 錯過良機

We really missed the boat this time! That deal would have made us millions. 這次我們真的錯失良機，這筆交易原可讓我們賺進幾百萬的。

moolah ［múlɑ］ 錢

I spent all my moolah. Now I'm broke. 我把所有的錢花光，現在我破產了。

moolah

mosey ［mózi］ along 閑逛

We don't have time to mosey along. We're late already! 我們沒時間閑逛，我們已經遲了。

motor-mouth 說話滔滔不絕的人（= chatterbox）

Cathy is such a motor-mouth. I can never get a word in. Cathy 說起話來滔滔不絕，我一句也插不進去。

mouth off 頂嘴

Don't mouth off at me young man! Where are your manners? 年輕人別頂嘴！你的禮貌那裡去了？

move in on   逐漸侵佔

Sharon was always trying to move in on Jane's boyfriend.
Sharon 總是想侵佔 Jane 的男朋友。

Frozen foods have moved in on the market for fresh poultry.
冷凍食品已經逐漸侵佔了新鮮家禽肉類市場。

move in on

nerd   無趣的人

Jack is such a nerd. All day long he studies.　Jack 眞無趣，
整天只會唸書。

nitty-gritty   細節；基本狀況

Let's get down to the nitty-gritty. I want to hear what happens next.　讓我們來了解詳細的情況，我想知道後來發生了什麼事。

no can do   不行

No can do. My calendar is booked for the next month.　不行
，我下個月的計劃全排滿了。

no big deal ／ no biggie   小事；沒什麼大不了

It's no big deal going to college. You'll see your parents on
the holidays.　上大學不是什麼大不了的事，你可以在假日見到你的父
母。

N

no good　很糟

This typewriter is no good. Every time I use it, the ribbon falls out.　這部打字機很糟，每次一用，色帶就掉下來。

no kidding　"不蓋你"；眞的啊?!

No kidding! I knew about it long before you did.　不蓋你，我比你早知道。

no sweat　不麻煩；沒問題

No sweat. I'll have the report done for you in an hour.　沒問題，我會在一小時之內爲你做出這份報告。

no sweat

not be caught dead　獻醜；出洋相

I wouldn't be caught dead in that ugly outfit.　我才不要穿那樣難看的衣服出去獻醜。

not by a long shot　絕不可能［long shot 指在 "遙遠處射箭"］

There's no way he could have won, not by a long shot.　他絕不會贏的。

no way Jose　［hozé］　絕對不行［Jose 爲西班牙的人名，此處只作押韻用］

No way Jose! I'm not going down that alley alone.　絕不幹！我絕不一個人走那條巷子。

number, do a number on   騙；作手脚；玩花樣

Susan really did a number on her hair. It looks like an orange porcupine is lying on her head. Susan 在頭髮上大動手脚，看起來像隻橘色的豪豬躺在她頭上。

do a number on

number, have someone's number   有…的底牌；看穿

She dare not do anything to me, because I have her number. 她不敢對我怎麼樣的，因為我對她的底牌一清二楚。

number, hot number   新鮮迷人的人或事物，"尤物"

Tom thinks Sheryl is a hot number.   Tom 認為 Sheryl 是個尤物。

off the hook   逃脫溜掉；不受罰

I'll let you off the hook this time, but don't be late again. 這次不罰你，下次不要再遲到了。

off the hook

off the top of one's head 不加思索；馬上

I can't tell you the information off the top of my head. I'll have to look it up. 我沒辦法馬上告訴你這個消息，我得查一下。

off-the-wall 古怪的；離奇的

He said some really off-the-wall things. Where does he come up with them? 他說了一些非常離奇的事，他從哪裡聽來的？

okey-doke [ókidók] 沒問題

Okey-doke, I'll be over in five minutes. 沒問題，我五分鐘就來。

on a roll 順利；手氣運氣好

Don't stop me now. I'm on a roll. 現在別叫我停，我手氣正好。

on the right track 走對路了

If you learn ten new vocabulary words every day, you're on the right track to speaking fluent English. 如果你每天學十個生字，就有希望把英語說得流利了。

The detective said, "We don't have many clues, but I think we're on the right track for finding the thief." 偵探說：「雖然我們線索不多，但我們在追查竊賊上的路線是對的。」

on the dot 準時

He arrived on the dot. I was sure he'd be late. 我以為他會遲到，他卻準時到了。

out in left field 瘋了

He's out in left field. Nobody ever understands what he is

talking about. 他必定瘋了，沒有人知道他在說些什麼。

✓ **out of it　迷迷糊糊；昏昏沈沈；心不在焉**

Sara's always out of it, she has no idea of what goes on in the world today. Sara 總是迷迷糊糊，現在世界發生什麼事她完全不知道。

One hour after the operation, she's still out of it. 開刀一小時之後，她還沒有完全清醒過來。

out of it

out of luck　運氣不好

You're out of luck; the last bus left half an hour ago. 你運氣不好，最後一班巴士半小時前就開走了。

out of luck

out of this world　太棒了；好極了 〔原意爲 "非人間物"〕

This food is out of this world. I'll have to get your recipe. 這道菜好極了！我要向你要食譜。

out of whack　壞了，有問題，走樣了。

This phone is out of whack. You can't dial out.　這部電話壞了，撥不出去。

out on a limb　處境危險；焦頭爛額

Sonya left Jimmy out on a limb after she stood him up at the altar.　Jimmy 在結婚聖壇前空等 Sonya（新娘），把他急得焦頭爛額。

over my dead body　絕不可能；休想

He asked me if he could take my girlfriend out for a date, but I told him, "Over my dead body!" so he gave up.　他問我能否和我的女朋友約會，我告訴他：「你休想！」，於是他就放棄了。

overkill　太誇張；殺雞用牛刀

She wore a brand-new cocktail dress to an informal afternoon tea party.　No wonder everyone accuses her of overkill.　她穿了全新的雞尾酒禮服參加非正式的下午茶會，難怪每個人都罵她太誇張了。

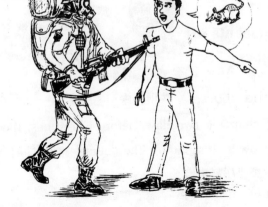

overkill

94

over the hill　走下坡

Grandpa is over the hill. He can't do as much as he thinks he can.　爺爺已經老了，不能隨心所欲做事。

pain in the neck ╱ ass　令人討厭的人或事

Jackie is a real pain in the neck. She's always butting into other people's business.　Jackie 真討厭，她總是愛多管閒事。

✓ pan out　成功；奏效

Unfortunately, the deal did not pan out. I lost a thousand dollars.　這筆生意不幸沒有成功，我損失了一千元。

pants, beat the pants off　打得落花流水

That team was not very good. We beat the pants off them. The final score was 21 − 3.　那支隊伍真爛，我們21比3把他們打得落花流水。

beat the pants off

✓ par for the course　在預料中

When shopping two days before Christmas, there's bound to be large crowds. It's par for the course.　聖誕節前兩天逛街一定是人山人海，這是意料中事。

P

party-pooper　掃興的人

Don't be such a party-pooper.　The night is still young.　別這麼掃興，夜晚才剛開始呢！

pass out　醉倒了

He passed out after three beers.　喝了三杯啤酒之後他就醉倒了。

pass something up　放棄

You can't pass up this job. This kind of opportunity comes only once in a lifetime.　你不可錯過這個工作，這種機會一輩子才有一次。

pass something up

passion, have a passion for　鍾愛；中意

Carol has a passion for blue dresses.　Carol喜愛藍色的衣服。

passion　"最愛"

My big passion in life is dancing.　舞蹈是我生活中的最愛。

peanuts　微薄的錢；蠅頭小利

Don't work for Mr. Hooper. The hours are long and the pay is peanuts.　不要替 Hooper 先生工作，工作既久，報酬又少。

peeve　惹惱

The way Carl acts like he owns the world really peeves me.
Carl 那副全世界都是他的樣子真讓我生氣。

penny-pincher　節省的人

Marge is a real penny-pincher. She doesn't spend money
unless it is absolutely necessary. Marge 真節省，除非真的需要，否
則她絕不花錢。

penny-pincher

pep talk　打氣；鼓勵的話

The coach gave his team a pep talk at half time, hoping to
lead them to victory.　教練在半場時候幫球員打打氣，希望他們能
贏球。

pet peeve　最厭惡的事

My biggest pet peeve is the way Seth slurps his soup. It
drives me crazy.　我討厭的是 Seth 吸湯的樣子，我看了會發瘋。

phony　假的

That cupboard does not open; it's a phony. It's there for
decoration.　那個櫃子打不開，是假的那是用來裝飾的。

pick someone's brains　請教

I don't understand any of this medical terminology. Do you

mind if I pick your brains since you're so knowledgeable in this area? 我對這個醫學術語一無所知，你在這一方面很在行，能不能請教你？

pick up the tab 付帳

It's my turn to pick up the tab. You treated last time. 現在輪到我付帳了，上次是你請的。

piece, in one piece 全身而退

The villagers escaped from the flood in one piece. 所有的村民都逃過了這次洪水，一點沒有受到傷害。

piece of cake 輕鬆愉快的事

That exam was a piece of cake. My studying really paid off. 考試真簡單，我的用功沒有白費。

piece of cake

piece, get a piece of the action 參加一份

To get a piece of the action, all you have to do is invest two thousand dollars. 你們只要投資兩千元就可參加一份。

piece, give...a piece of one's mind　痛罵

Johnny is over three hours late and he hasn't called. I'm going to give him a piece of my mind when he gets home.

Johnny 已經遲到三個小時還沒打電話來，他一回家我要好好罵他一頓。

pig out　狼吞虎嚥

We pigged out on potato chips and cookies until our bellies ached.　我們大吃洋芋片和餅乾吃到肚子痛。

pissed off　生氣

I'm really pissed off at Harry. He took the credit for all my work.　我實在對 Harry 很生氣，我拚命工作他却坐享其成。

pissed off

pit stop　（為上廁所）暫停

Can we make a pit stop? Paula really needs to go to the bathroom.　暫停一下好嗎？Paula 要上洗手間。

plastic　信用卡

I hope they take plastic at this restaurant. I don't have any cash on me.　我希望這家餐廳可以用信用卡，我沒帶現金。

play dirty　耍詐

The only way that Dan knows how to win is to play dirty.
I'm going to vote for Brian instead.　Dan 只會用耍詐來贏，我要
投 Brian 一票。

play dirty

play games　搞鬼

Don't play games with me, Jane. I'm on to your tricks and
manipulations.　Jane，別跟我搞鬼，我對你的詭計和手段一清
二楚。

✓ play it by ear　看狀況行事；見機行事；走著瞧

I didn't get the report until just a few minutes ago. I'll have
to play it by ear in the meeting today.　幾分鐘前我才拿到報告，今
天的會議只有見機行事了。

play second fiddle　居次位

Jack doesn't like playing second fiddle to anyone. He always
strives to be number one.　Jack 不喜歡輸給別人，他處處搶第一。

play it safe　謹慎行事

It's better to play it safe than make a hasty move that
we'll regret later on.　我們最好謹慎行事，別做出事後會後悔的莽撞
行動。

poke one's nose into something　多管閒事

Gladys is always poking her nose into other people's business. I don't see how she has time to take care of her own affairs.　Gladys 總是愛管閒事，我不知道她怎麼會有時間處理自己的事。

poke one's nose into something

polish off　狼吞虎嚥；吃光

We were so hungry that we polished off Mom's apple pie in ten minutes.　我們餓死了，十分鐘就把媽媽的蘋果餅吃得精光。

poo　糟了

Oh poo! I forgot to mail the letter I wrote last night.　糟了！我忘了寄出昨晚寫好的信。

pooped out　累壞了

I'm pooped out. We must have jogged five miles today.　我累壞了，我們今天肯定跑了五哩路了。

pop one's cork　大發脾氣

I've never seen Teresa pop her cork before. I always thought she was a very laid back person.　我從沒見過 Teresa 發脾氣，我一直以為她是個好好小姐。

potluck　聚餐〔各家帶一道菜的聚餐方式〕

We're having a potluck Friday night, so bring a dish to pass.
星期五晚上我們要聚餐，帶一道菜來參加吧！

pour money down the drain　亂花錢

Fran is always buying things that she has no use for. I don't see how she can pour money down the drain like that.　Fran 總是買沒有用的東西，我不知道她為什麼那樣亂花錢。

powwow〔páuwau〕　討論

The manager would like to have a powwow with you today to discuss your project.　經理希望今天和你談談你的計劃。

pronto　立刻；馬上〔源自西班牙文〕

Give me that report pronto! I needed it yesterday.　立刻把報告給找！我其實昨天就要了。

psych oneself up　振奮精神；使自己進入情況

Before each performance, Beth listens to classical music to psych herself up for the concert.　每次音樂會表演之前，Beth 聽古典音樂來使自己進入情況。

pull a fast one

pull a fast one　欺騙

He tried to pull a fast one on us, but we caught on before he got away with it.　他想要欺騙我們，但在他陰謀得逞前就被我們逮到了。

pull it off (= make it) 成功

We weren't sure the business would survive past the first month, but we pulled it off. 我們並不確定生意會熬過第一個月，然而我們卻熬過來了。

pull rank 擺出高姿態

Don't try to pull rank on me. We're all equals here. 別對我擺高姿態，這裡人人平等。

pull rank

pull someone's leg 開某人玩笑

He told me he was only twenty years old. I think he was pulling my leg. 他告訴我他才二十歲，我想他在開我玩笑。

pull strings 運用關係〔源自 "拉木偶的線"〕

He pulled some strings and managed to get us front row seats for the concert. 他運用關係替我們拿到音樂會第一排的位子。

pull the plug on 不再支持〔原意爲 "拔掉揷頭"〕

If the ratings don't go up soon, they're going to pull the plug on this show. 如果收視率不快點上升，他們就不再支持這個節目了。

pull the wool over someone's eyes　矇騙

She tried to pull the wool over his eyes, but he didn't fall for it.　她想矇騙他，他卻沒上當。

pump iron　舉重

You can really tell that Paul has been pumping iron recently.　He works out every day after work. 你可以看出 Paul 最近一直在舉重，他每天下班後都出去做運動。

pump iron

pump up （＝ psych up ）　熱切期待

Everybody on campus is pumped up about Saturday's big game. The winning team will get the national title.　校園裡大家都熱切期待星期六的大賽，贏的隊伍將是全國冠軍。

punch line　好笑的部份

I can't tell the joke; I forgot the punch line.　我無法說這個笑話，我忘了當中最好笑的部份。

punch someone's lights out　痛打

If you tell anybody the secret I told you, I'll punch your lights out.　如果你告訴別人我對你所說的秘密，我會把你的眼睛都打出來。

push around　欺負

Don't try to push me around!　別想欺負我！

push comes to shove　事態嚴重

When push comes to shove, only your true friends will still stand by you.　當事態嚴重時，只有真正的朋友還會支持你。

push one's button　惹火；激怒

Nobody makes me as mad as Dave does. He really knows how to push my buttons.　沒有人像 Dave 那樣讓我生氣。他真知道怎麼惹我發火。

pushover　容易使喚的人；好好先生

Tiffany is such a pushover. She'll do anything anybody tells her to do.　Tiffany 真是一個容易使喚的人，她一天到晚被人牽着鼻子走。

pushover

pussycat　乖乖牌

Don't mind Larry. He won't hurt you. He's a pussycat.　別擔心 Larry，他不會傷害你，他是一個乖乖牌。

put a move on　挑逗

He tried to put the moves on her, but she turned him down. 他想要挑逗她，但她不假以辭色。

put away　大吃大喝

I've never seen anybody put away so much food and still look so thin.　我從未見這麼會吃的人還這麼瘦。

put-down　羞辱，貶損

I've had enough of your put-downs. You're not perfect either. 我受夠了你的羞辱，你也好不到那裡去。

put one's ass on the line　兩肋插刀；不惜一切

I put my ass on the line for you. I know you'll do the same for me someday.　我為你兩肋插刀，我知道將來你也會為我這麼做。

put one's ass on the line

put one's finger on something　確切認出

I can't put my finger on it, but I know I've seen you before. 我知道我曾經見過你，但記不起到底是在什麼地方。

put one's foot in one's mouth　亂說話惹麻煩；禍從口出

Wally is always saying such stupid thing. He has a real talent for putting his foot in his mouth.　Wally 儘說些這類的蠢話，他真有惹是生非的本事。

put one's money where one's mouth is　說到做到

If you're so sure of yourself, why don't you put your money where your mouth is.　如果你對自己那麼有把握，爲什麼你不能說到做到呢？

put one's two cents in　提供個人僅有的、微不足道的資源

Carrie always puts her two cents in. Sometimes her advice is helpful.　Carrie 總是提供她僅有的，有時候她的建議還眞管用。

put on airs　擺架子

I can't stand Mary. She's always putting on airs because she thinks she's better than everybody else.　我實在受不了 Mary，她老擺架子，因爲她自以爲比別人好。

put on airs

put （something） on the line　賠上；不惜

I'd gladly put my reputation on the line for you. You're my closest friend.　我願意爲你賠上我的名譽，你是我最好的朋友。

put someone on the spot　讓人爲難

Don't put me on the spot like this. You know I can't give you confidential information.　別這樣讓我爲難，你知道我不能給你機密資料的。

put someone up　留宿

I can put you up for a couple of days. My apartment is big enough for two people.　你可以在我這裡住幾天，我的公寓可以住兩個人。

put someone out　替人增加麻煩

Please don't go to so much trouble. I don't want to put you out.　請不要費那麼多工夫，我不想增加你的麻煩。

put up with (someone or something)　忍受

How do you put up with all her annoying habits?　你怎麼可以忍受她那些討厭的習慣。

quickie　匆忙的；快的

I'm running late. I only have time for a quickie shower.　我快遲到了，只好沖個快澡。

racket　非法行業，"掛羊頭賣狗肉"

Mr. Howard's racket was selling broken vacuum cleaners. Howard 先生賣壞的吸塵器欺騙顧客。

The police are determined to break up the racket.　警方決心打擊這個非法行業。

racket

rag　爛報

The National Enquirer is a real rag.　National Enquirer 眞是一份大爛報。

rain check　改天再做

I can't make it to dinner tonight because I already made other plans. Can I have a rain check though?　我今晚有事不能去吃晚飯，改天再吃好不好？

rain on someone's parade　掃興

Today is Janie's birthday. Don't rain on her parade. 今天是Janie 的生日，別掃她的興。

rain on someone's parade

rap　饒舌歌〔一種快而押韻的朗誦，類似"順口溜"，可配上音樂、舞蹈，八〇年代在美國黑人少年中非常流行〕

Do you like rap music? I have trouble understanding the words.　你喜歡 rap 音樂嗎？我聽不太懂其中的歌詞。

rap sheet　犯罪紀錄；前科

This isn't his first offense. He has a rap sheet a mile long. 這不是他第一次犯罪，他前科累累。

raw deal　卑鄙的行為

What a raw deal! I deserve the promotion more than he does.　卑鄙！我比他更應該升職。

read someone like a book　熟悉某人

We've known each other so long that I can read her like a book.　我們認識好久了，我對她一清二楚。

read my lips　注意聽

Read my lips. I don't like broccoli.　注意聽，我不喜歡綠花椰菜。

read my lips

red carpet　隆重歡迎［原意為 "紅地毯"］

Bring out the red carpet; the governor is coming to town. 州長進城了，我們要隆重歡迎。

red-letter day　大日子

This is a red-letter day for Susan; she made her first sale to a very important client.　今天是 Susan 的大日子，她和一個重要客戶做成了第一筆生意。

red tape 官樣文章；煩瑣的程序

I need this information as soon as possible. See if you can cut through the red tape. 我要儘快拿到這份文件，看能不能縮短申請的程序。

red tape

retard 白痴

What a retard! She can't do anything right. 她真是個白痴！什麼都做不好。

rev up 刺激；振奮

This party is pretty dead. We need to rev it up a little. 這個舞會死氣沈沈，我們得把氣氛炒熱。

right off the bat 立刻

I was all prepared to put up a fight, but she gave in right off the bat. 我正準備和她大打一場，但是她馬上就投降了。

right up there 不亞於；並駕其驅

Her name is right up there with all the other big shots. 她的名字和其他大人物一樣響亮。

ring off the hook　電話鈴聲不斷

I couldn't get any work done this morning because the phone kept ringing off the hook.　今天早上電話一直響個不停，我什麼事都不能做。

ripoff　騙人的東西

What a ripoff! The new toaster oven I bought doesn't work. 眞是個騙人貨！我新買的烤箱不能用。

rock the boat　找麻煩

Don't rock the boat.　Things are fine just the way they are. 別找麻煩了，事情這樣就夠好了。

rock the boat

roll with the punches　逆來順受

You have to roll with the punches if you want to survive in this business.　如果你要在這一行生存下去的話，就得逆來順受。

room, no room to talk　沒有資格講話

Mary came in to work 15 minutes late. Five minutes later,

Nancy came rushing in. Mary said, "I hate it when people are late to work." Mary's friend, Bertha, said, "Mary, you have no room to talk!" Mary 上班晚了十五分鐘，五分鐘後 Nancy 衝進來，Mary 說，「我討厭人家上班遲到。」Mary 的朋友 Bertha 說，「Mary，你沒資格批評別人。」

round up　集合

Round everybody up. It's time for our business meeting. 叫大家集合，開會時間到了。

rub elbows　交際；接觸

It's important for you to go to these parties and rub elbows with everyone. That's how contacts are made. 參加這些宴會交際交際是很重要的，關係就是這樣建立起來的。

rub elbows

rub it in　火上加油

You don't have to rub it in. I already feel bad enough as it is. 你不要再火上加油了，我已經夠難過的。

rub it in

run, give the runaround ①忙得團團轉 ②兜圈子應付，"打太極拳"

① I had to go to four different departments to get the dress I needed. Those salespeople really gave me the runaround. 我走了四個部門才買到我要的衣服，那些店員真會讓我團團轉。

② Martha doesn't want to go to the dance with Tom, so every time he asks her about it, she gives him the runaround. Martha 不想和 Tom 去那個舞會，因此每次他邀她去，她就打太極拳。

run something by again 重複

Can you run that by again? I didn't quite understand your last point. 請再說一遍好嗎？最後一點我聽不太懂。

Russian roulette 玩命的事〔原意為 "俄羅斯輪盤"〕

Drinking and driving is like playing Russian roulette. 酒後開車簡直是玩命。

Russian roulette

sappy　靡靡之音

This is such a stupid song. How can you listen to sappy music like this? 這真是一首爛歌，你怎麼會聽這樣的靡靡之音呢？

sauce, the sauce　酒

After her mother's death, she started hitting the sauce again. 她媽媽死了之後，她又開始酗酒。

says who　誰說的？［不相信的語氣］

This outfit doesn't match? Says who? 這套衣服不相配？誰說的？

says who

say what　你說什麼？

Say what? I didn't hear what you said. 你說什麼？我沒聽到。

scam　騙局

The accountant thought he had a clever scam to steal money from his company, but his boss found out. 會計想從公司騙錢，卻被老闆發現了。

scared stiff　嚇死了

That was a great horror movie. I was scared stiff. 那部恐

怖電影眞棒，把我嚇死了。

scare the daylights ／ shit out of（smoeone） 嚇死了

Don't sneak up behind me like that. You scared the day-lights out of me. 不要從後面突然嚇我，你把我嚇死了。

scare the daylights

scatterbrain 心不在焉；迷糊

What a scatterbrain! She forgot to plug in the coffee maker. 眞是迷蝴！她忘了給咖啡壺插電。

schmuck ［ʃmʌk］ 討厭鬼

Ken is a real schmuck. That's why nobody likes him. Ken 眞是個討厭鬼，所以沒人喜歡他。

screw around 鬼混

We don't have time to screw around. We have a deadline to meet. 我們沒時間鬼混了，我們要趕最後的期限。

screw loose 脫線

Bill must have a screw loose somewhere; he's acting really strangely. Bill 必定那根筋不對，他的舉動眞奇怪。

screw someone over 欺負

After working in the office for ten years, Alice was fired for no apparent reason.   How can they screw her over like that? Alice 工作了十年之後，無緣無故被炒魷魚，他們怎麼可以這樣欺負她呢？

screw someone over

screw up 弄錯

The hotel screwed up our reservations so we didn't have a room for the night. 旅社把我們預訂的房間弄錯，我們晚上沒有地方可住了。

screw you 去你的

Screw you! I don't need you to tell me what to do. 去你的！我不需要你告訴我怎麼做。

scrounge up 想辦法獲取

I'm out of white paper. See if you can scrounge up a few sheets for me.   我的白紙用完了，能不能替我弄一些來。

second guess 猜測

Television networks are always trying to second guess the public. 電視公司總是在預測大眾的口味。

second, get one's second wind 適應；進入情況

After the first quarter mile, a runner usually gets his second wind and can breathe better. 跑完四分之一哩之後，跑者通常可以進入情況，呼吸得順一點。

Tom was very tired of working at his algebra, but after a while he got his second wind and began to enjoy it. Tom 很討厭做代數題目，但是適應後也就喜歡了。

second wind

sell someone on something 以...說服...

She sold me on her idea. I think it will work. 她以她的看法說服了我，我想那行得通。

set oneself up as 做起...（職業）；當起...

After graduating from college, Larry set himself up as a businessman. 大學畢業後，Larry 做起生意來了。

set someone back 使...花費

That dinner set me back sixty dollars. 那頓晚飯花了我六十元。

shake a leg　趕快

Shake a leg!　We're already ten minutes late.　快點！我們已遲到十分鐘了。

shape up　表現良好；乖

You'd better shape up if you want to stay on.　如果你還想留下來的話你最好乖一點。

sheesh〔ʃiʃ〕或〔ʒiʃ〕　〔討厭的表示〕

Sheesh!　Can't you do anything by yourself?　噓！你不能自己做一點事嗎？

shindig〔ʃíndɪg〕　盛大的舞會

This is a great shindig!　I haven't had this much fun in quite some time.　真是個了不起的舞會！我好久沒有這麼開心了。

shoo-in　常勝軍

There's no way he can lose; he's a shoo-in.　他不會輸的，他是一個常勝軍。

shoo-in

(all) shook up　張皇失措

What did he say to her?　She's all shook up. 他跟她說了些什麼使她這麼張皇失措？

shoot from the hip　坦率爽朗；一根腸子通到底

I like Mandy because she shoots from the hip.　She says what's on her mind.　我喜歡 Mandy，因爲她坦率爽朗，會說出心中的話。

short end of the stick　倒楣

I'm so unlucky; I always end up with the short end of the stick.　我運氣不佳老走霉運。

short end of the stick

shot, a fair shot　濃厚的希望

You have a fair shot at the scholarship. 你很有希望得到獎學金。

show-off　愛現的人

Jim is such a show-off.　Who is he trying to impress?　Jim 是個愛現的人，他又在向誰賣弄了？

shut out 讓對手掛零

The Tigers shut out the Orioles five to zip. 老虎隊以五比○大勝金鶯隊。

skid row 爛地區

If you don't quit drinking, you'll end up sleeping on skid row. 如果你不戒酒，最後你一定會在這種爛地區過夜。

sit tight 耐心等待

Just sit tight. The doctor will be with you in a minute. 耐心等一下，醫生馬上就來看你。

sleazebag ／ sleazeball 渾球

Walter is a real sleazebag. He comes on to every girl he sees. Walter 真是渾球，他一看到女孩，就想吃豆腐。

sleazebag

sloshed 酩酊大醉

Tom's wife was furious when he came home sloshed. Tom 喝得爛醉回家，他太太很生氣。

small potatoes　①小錢　②小角色；小人物

① This is small potatoes compared to the money we're going to make.　這和我們將要賺的錢比起來簡直微不足道。

② I cannot say yes or no. I'm just a small potato.　我不能決定，我只是小角色。

smart　耍；對師長無禮

Don't be smart with me, young man! 別耍我了！年輕人！

He was punished for smarting off to the principal. 他因為對校長無禮被處罰。

smart

snap out of it　振作起來

Snap out of it!　Why are you feeling sorry for yourself?　振作起來！你為何垂頭喪氣呢？

snappy　乾脆一點；直截了當

Make it snappy!　I don't have all day.　乾脆一點！我沒有時間耗下去了。

sob story　悲傷的事情

Her sob story really moved me.　It's so sad.　她悲傷的故事非常感動我，真令人難過呀！

softie　善良的人

Samantha is such a softie.　She doesn't have a mean bone in her.　Samantha 真善良，她心裡沒有一絲惡意。

son of a bitch　王八蛋

That son of a bitch stole my wallet!　那個王八蛋偷了我的皮夾！

son of a bitch

so-so　不怎麼樣

The movie I saw last night was so-so.　It wasn't worth the five dollars.　我昨晚看的電影並不怎樣，不值得花五塊錢。

so what　那又怎樣？

You're right. I don't have a date tonight. So what?　沒錯，我今晚沒有約會，那又怎樣？

spaced out　魂不守舍

He didn't hear what you said.　He's spaced out.　他沒聽到你說的話，他魂不守舍。

spaz-out / spastic［spǽztɪk］　緊張，"鷄飛狗跳"

Don't spaz-out.　It's really no big deal.　別緊張，沒什麼要緊。

Take it easy.　Don't get spastic.　慢慢來，別緊張。

speechless　（高興得）說不出話來

He was speechless after we told him he had gotten the job.
我們告訴他他得到這份工作時，他高興得說不出話來。

speechless

spill the beans　洩露祕密

Don't spill the beans. It's supposed to be a secret. 別說溜了嘴，這是個秘密哦！

spring for　請客

Let me spring for dinner. 讓我請客吃晚飯。

stand someone up　爽約；讓人空等

Paul didn't even call Amy to explain why he stood her up on Friday. Paul 甚至沒有打電話給 Amy 解釋他上星期五為什麼失約。

stand someone up

stay out of it　不介入

I'm going to stay out of their argument.　我不打算介入他們的
爭執。

step on it　趕快〔it 指油門〕

Carol told the driver to step on it because she didn't want to
miss her plane.　Carol 告訴司機快一點，因為她不想錯過飛機。

step on it

stick around　①在附近等待；②逗留

①I think I'll stick around the house for a while.　我想我會在
房子附近待一會兒。

②Stick around. The fun is just beginning!　別走，好玩的才剛
開始呢！

stick around

stick in the mud　保守的人

Ginny is such a stick in the mud.　She never wants to try
anything new.　Ginny 真保守，她從不想嘗試新的東西。

stink 討厭

It really stinks that we have to work during the holidays. 我們連假日都得工作，真討厭。

stir-crazy 發瘋，"抓狂"

I wish it would stop raining. I'm going stir-crazy being cooped up in this house. 希望雨快點停，我整天關在家裡都快發瘋了。

store, in store ①準備好 ②註定會

① A typhoon is coming tomorrow, so we're all in store for a day of heavy rain and winds. 明天颱風就要來了，因此我們都準備好應付一天的狂風暴雨。

② If we aren't careful, those kinds of problems will be in store for us. 我們如果不小心，就註定會碰到那些問題的。

straight face 面無表情

He can never tell a joke with a straight face. 他總是無法面無表情地說笑話。

straight face

streak, a blue streak 很快的；機關槍似的

My grandmother could talk a blue streak when she wanted to. 我祖母可以機關槍似的說話。

string someone along　欺騙；對...賣關子

Don't string me along.　Tell me exactly where things stand now.　別騙我了，告訴我東西在什麼地方。

stuck-up　傲慢自大

Nobody likes him because he is so stuck-up. 他這麼傲慢自大，沒人喜歡他。

suck　爛

Don't buy things from that store. It sucks. 別去那家店買東西，那家店很爛。

suck eggs　①可惡　②爛（= suck）

How could they cancel the concert? This really sucks eggs! 他們怎麼可以取消演唱會呢？眞可惡！

suck up to someone　拍馬屁（= brown-nose）

Ron gets ahead by sucking up to the boss.　Ron 因拍馬屁而升官。

suck up to someone

sucker　白痴

What a sucker! He bought five acres of real estate, then he found out the land is in the middle of a desert.　他真是個白痴！買了五英畝地，卻發現那些地在沙漠中間。

sure thing　十拿九穩的事

This bet is a sure thing.　You can't lose.　這次賭注你必定會贏，不會輸的。

sure thing

sweep off one's feet　（因感情因素）令人神魂顛倒

He's handsome, he's intelligent, and best of all, he is rich. No wonder he swept me off my feet.　I think I'm in love! 他英俊、聰明又多金，難怪他會令我神魂顛倒，我想我愛上他了。

take a shine to　有好感

He really likes you.　There are very few people he takes a shine to right away.　他真的喜歡你，他很少對人一見面就有好感的。

take care of business　負責

Who's going to take care of business while I'm away? 我不在的時候，誰負責啊？

take it easy　放鬆；休息

You should take it easy for a while. You've been working too hard. 你該休息一下，你一直工作太辛苦了。

take （it） out on　拿…出氣

Don't take your frustrations out on me.　別把氣出在我身上。

take the rap　代爲受過

I can't let you take the rap for something that I did.　我不能讓你爲我做的事代爲受過。

tapped out　破產

I'm all tapped out. Can you loan me five dollars? 我完全破產了，借我五塊錢好不好？

tapped out

tell it like it is　實話實說

Jenny doesn't beat around the bush; she just tells it like it is. Jenny 不拐彎抹角，她實話實說。

thingamajig 〔θíŋmədʒɪg〕 （叫不出名字的）東西

To make it start, you just pull this thingamajig out. 要起動，你先把這個東西拉出來

third wheel 累贅；"電燈泡"

You two go on ahead. I don't want to be a third wheel. 你們兩個去好了，我不想當電燈泡。

throw a fit 大發脾氣

Becky threw a fit when Richard cancelled their weekend plans. Richand 取消他們週末的節目時，Becky 大發脾氣。

throw a fit

throw one's hat in the ring 宣布參選

Gerald didn't like any of the candidates that were running, so he decided to throw his own hat in the ring. Gerald 不喜歡任何候選人，因此他決定自己參選。

throw in the towel 放棄；投降

It's too early to throw in the towel. There's still hope. 現在放棄太早了，仍然有希望啊！

tide over 救急

I ran out of money before payday, so my father loaned me $2000 to tide me over. 在發薪水前我把錢用光了，因此父親借我 2000 元救急。

top-drawer ／ top-notch 第一流的

This restaurant is top-drawer. They serve the best food in town. 這家餐廳是第一流的，他們供應全鎮最好的食物。

toss-up 不分軒輊

It's a toss-up between George and Carl; both candidates are good. George 和 Carl 兩位候選人都很好，讓人很難選擇。

toss-up

total 全毀

He totaled his mother's car while driving intoxicated. 他喝醉了開車，把他媽媽的車撞得稀爛。

turn in 上床睡覺

I'm so tired. I think I'll just turn in and see you in the morning. 我累死了，我想我要去睡覺了，明天見。

turn someone off 使...倒胃口；使...厭惡

I was turned off by his rude manners. 我厭惡他粗魯的行為。

twist someone's arm　勉強，好說歹說地要

I wasn't going to come, but he twisted my arm.　我不想來，他卻好說歹說地要我來。

under the weather　生病；不舒服

I'm feeling a little under the weather today.　I think I'll go home early.　我今天有點不舒服，想早點回去。

up, on the up and up　光明正大；誠實無欺

I checked out his story; he's on the up and up.　我查過他的資料，他誠實可靠。

up for grabs　①職位空置等人遞補　②一片混亂等待整理

①Now that Mr. Reynolds is retiring, his position is up for grabs. Reynolds 先生要退休了，他的位置空下來等人去搶。

②I just moved in.　This place is still up for grabs.　我剛搬進來，這個地方很亂，有待整理。

up for grabs

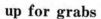

up front　預先

In order to hold your reservation, I'll need a 10% down payment up front.　為了保留你的預訂，我要先收 10% 的訂金。

up in the air　懸而未決

Why did Charles leave so suddenly?　All his affairs are up in the air.　Charles 爲何那樣匆匆離去？　他的事情都還沒有搞定呢。

up shit creek　慘兮兮

If Mom catches you smoking in the house,　you'll　be up shit creek.　如果你在家裡抽煙讓媽逮到，你就慘了。

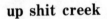

up shit creek

up to here　受夠了

I've had it up to here with all your complaining.　If you hate your job that much, just quit.　我聽夠了你的抱怨，要是你那麼恨你的工作，那就辭掉算了。

uppity〔ˊʌpətɪ〕　自命不凡

Don't be so uppity.　You don't think we're good enough for you?　不要那麼自以爲了不起，你認爲我們配不上你嗎？

use one's head　動腦筋

If you'd use your head once in a while, you wouldn't get into such messes.　如果你稍微動一下腦筋的話，事情就不會這麼一團糟。

walk out on　丟開不管

You can't walk out on me; I really need your help.　你不能丟下我不管，我正需要你的幫助。

washed up ／ all washed up　①完了　②戒毒（＝ clean ）

① I'm all washed up.　I haven't been able to come up with a new invention in over a year.　我全完了，整整一年都沒有新發明。

② Don't worry.　He's already washed up.　別擔心，他已經戒毒了。

washed up

way back　好久以前

We've been friends since way back.　我們老早就是好朋友了。

weirdo　怪物

There's a weirdo in my neighborhood who always talks to himself as if he's having an argument. I think he's really sick. 我隔壁那個怪物經常自言自語好像和人爭辯一樣，我想他真的有病。

whatchamacallit　叫不出名字的東西［源自 " what you may call it "］

Bring me the whatchamacallit so I can loosen this bolt.　把那東西拿給我，我要放鬆這個螺絲。

what's his name　不知名的小子

Tell what's his name to run an errand for me.　告訴那小子替我做件事。

what's up　如何？怎樣？

Hi! I haven't seen you around in a while.　What's up?　好久不見，近來如何？

where it's at ／ where the action is　好玩的地方

If you're looking for a good time, ask Tim.　He knows where the action is.　如果你有時間就告訴 Tim，他知道那裡好玩。

willies , the willies　毛骨悚然

Watching horror movies gives me the willies.　看恐怖電影讓我毛骨悚然。

wimp　"軟骨頭"；沒用的傢伙

Harold is a real wimp.　He lets everbody take advantage of him.　Harold 真沒用，每個人都可以佔他便宜。

wimp

wind something up　結束

We'd better wind this meeting up.　It's getting pretty late.
我們最好結束這個會議，現在已經很晚了。

wing　即興作(= ad lib)

Don't worry; you'll be great.　If you forget a line, just wing
it.　別擔心，你很棒，如果你忘了詞，就隨口編吧！

wishy-washy　脚踏兩條船；猶豫不決

Don't be so wishy-washy.　You have to take a stand one
way or the other.　別再猶豫不決了，你必須有所選擇。

word, in every sense of the word　不折不扣的；道道地地的

Sherly is a professional in every sense of the word.　Sherly
是個道道地地的專家。

words, run out of words　無話可說

He talked easily with most people, but around Jane he often
ran out of words and was silent.　他可以輕鬆地與多數人聊天，但
是一碰到 Jane，就一句話也說不出來了。

run out of words

words, take the words out of someone's mouth 說出別人心中的話；正中下懷

When Sally said she was tired of homework, she took the words right out of my mouth.　Sally 說不想做功課時，正說中了我的心事。

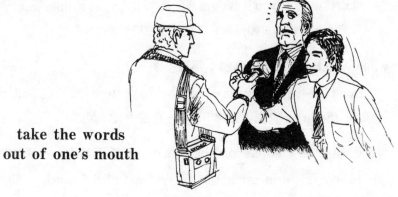

take the words out of one's mouth

work one's tail off 盡力而爲

I worked my tail off on this project.　The boss better appreciate it.　我費盡心血做這項計劃，希望老闆能欣賞。

work something out 把某事做成

I'm sure we can work this out.　There are only a few details that need to be ironed out.　我保證我們可以把這件事情做成，現在只剩一些細節要解決。

work out 運動；做體操

Jill works out for forty-five minutes every morning.　Jill 每天早上運動四十五分鐘。

world-class　世界級水準

This is a world-class hotel.　All the important people stay here when they're in town.　這是家世界級旅館，大人物來都住在這裡。

worry wart　杞人憂天的人

Don't be such a worry wart; you have to learn how to relax. 別杞人憂天了，你要學會看開一點。

worry wart

wrap up　完成(＝ wind up)

Let's wrap this up in the next five minutes so we can all go home.　我們用五分鐘做完，就可以回家了。

write off　結束；取消

The restaurant owner finally wrote off his failing business and sold the property to a washateria.　這家餐廳生意失敗，終於結束營業，頂給了一家洗衣店。

you'd better believe something　不必說；必定

Do I cook? You'd better believe I do.　我會煮菜嗎？　那還用說！

you can't win 'em all　不可能每項都贏

Don't worry. You'll get them next time.　You can't win 'em all!　別難過，下次你會成功，你不可能每項都贏的嘛！

yuck / yucky 難吃

This meal tastes yuck！Who burned it？　這道菜眞難吃！誰燒壞的？

zero in on　集中注意力

To figure out what the problem is, we're going to have to zero in on this area. 爲了要找出問題所在，我們必須集中注意力在這一點上。

zero in

zit　青春痘

Why is it that every time I have a hot date, I break out with a big zit on my face?　爲什麼每次我有重要約會時，臉上都會冒出青春痘呢？

zone out　避開；隔掉

Living in New York City, you learn how to zone out the noises around you.　住在 New York 市，你必須學會對週圍的躁音聽而不聞。

zone out

zonk out　筋疲力盡；睡著

Bobby wanted to stay up to watch the late night movie, but he zonked out five minutes after it started.　Bobby 昨晚想撐著看晚場電影，但是開演才五分鐘就睡著了。

書林語言工具書

字彙研習及測驗 1,2,3,4,5	Kon, T.S. ⋯60＋60＋80＋80＋80
克漏字測驗 1,2,3	Wong, Julie ⋯⋯⋯80＋80＋100

■ 彩圖本兒童讀物

動物卡通畫冊（中英對照・全套十冊）	Gress, A.／書林 ⋯⋯⋯⋯400
爲什麼兔子沒有尾巴（中英對照）	Satin／書林 ⋯⋯⋯⋯60
龜兔賽跑（中英對照）	Satin／書林 ⋯⋯⋯⋯60
上學（中英對照）	Satin／書林 ⋯⋯⋯⋯60
虎姑婆與兔奶奶（中英對照）	Satin／書林 ⋯⋯⋯⋯60

最新美國成語詞典

本書是專爲非以英語爲母語的讀者而
編的，收錄美國成語五千條，舉例完
備，釋義精確，類似及相關成語亦有
互見，對於查考及增進英文能力極有
幫助。

23×16 cm，400 pp　　　　　200 元

常用美國成語手冊

收錄 1500 個生動有趣的美國成語，解
釋明確，例句豐富，對增進英文理解
及表達能力極有幫助。

19×13 cm，310 pp　　　　　120 元